THE BOYS' BOOK OF MAGNETISM

A STRING OF MAGNETIC BEADS

Steel balls taken from a worn out ball bearing are lined up on a small board by the aid of a groove. All of the balls seen in the photograph can be picked up as a string if you have steady nerves and a steady hand. That is where the fun comes in.

THE BOYS' BOOK OF
MAGNETISM

REVISED EDITION

By

RAYMOND F. YATES

Illustrated with Photographs

HARPER & ROW, PUBLISHERS
NEW YORK, EVANSTON, AND LONDON

CONTENTS

ILLUSTRATIONS

Illustrations

Illustrations

FOREWORD

WE HAVE often heard it said that no one knows what electricity is. That is quite true but there are other equally deep mysteries in science, and magnetism is one of them. Strangely enough, and perhaps quite surprising to the reader of this book, magnetism is a kin of electricity and it follows it wherever it may go: through our telephones, our radios, electric refrigerators, motors and batteries. Often the relationship between the two is so close that we cannot tell where one begins and the other leaves off. It can also be said that one of these forces cannot exist independently of the other.

And magnetism, as we shall soon find out, is an endlessly fascinating thing with which to experiment. In other fields of science, considerable equipment is needed. This is not so with magnetism. The work outlined in this book will keep you busy and interested for many weeks and yet it involves only the simplest materials, most of them to be found about the household. You can also make toys guided and controlled by the mysterious forces of magnetism. A new form of magic is also possible, and then there is the delightful adventure of discovering for ourselves the strange relationship between the two major forces in the world, electricity and magnetism. There is a lot of fun ahead!

THE BOYS' BOOK OF MAGNETISM

Chapter 1

WE LIVE ON A MAGNET

ALTHOUGH we literally live on a magnet and make wide and practical use of magnetism, we do not really understand this strange force. And it *is* a strange force. Let us not make a mistake about that. Commonplace; yes. But obvious; never! It is a great and all-pervading ghost-power that spreads its invisible tentacles throughout the whole universe. Even as we sit reading this modest contribution to the literature of magnetism, this queer force is constantly passing through our bodies in never-ending streams. We could not avoid it even if we wished and somehow or other, perhaps intuitively, we come to realize that the full answer to this ghost of the universe lies deep in the mystery of life itself.

In the practical, workaday world, magnetism and magnets are at our elbows no matter where we turn. There would be no electricity as we know it today without the complementary force of magnetism. Without magnetism, there would be no telephone, no radio, no television, no electric lights, no electric transportation or electric factory power. Indeed, electricity and magnetism are, we might say, the two faces of a single coin.

The early Greeks, wandering through the rock-strewn valleys of Magnesia, picked up heavy black stones that possessed the mysterious power of attracting and holding small pieces of iron. It was all very wonderful and not a little confusing to these ancient fellows but they did nothing about it except marvel, shrug their shoulders and pass along to the more practical problems of life.

Not so with the Chinese. It is not known when they came upon these invisible forces radiating outward from certain black stones. It is known, however, that they discovered that elongated stones of this kind, when suspended by a string, always pointed due north. Who the ancient Edison was is lost in antiquity but for nearly a thousand years now, men have guided ships at sea by means of compasses and compasses are nothing more or less than magnets so suspended that they invariably point north and thereby serve as references. Really, it is not quite as simple as it sounds but in this book we shall ferret out many interesting facts and sooner or later certain matters will become self-evident without lengthy explanation.

These black stones are really not stones at all. They are pieces of certain kinds of iron ore found in Asia Minor. The English later called them lodestones which meant way-stone or leading stone because such stones could be so arranged that they would show the way to sailors. More than that, they could attract and hold to themselves, as if by the aid of some sort of magic but invisible adhesive, bits of iron and steel. Stranger yet, the steel, upon contact with the lodestone, became magnetized itself and it could then both attract other pieces of steel and pass the property along! Little wonder that the ancient experimenters scratched their heads and gave up trying to understand this strange force. And our modern scientists are *still* scratching their heads!

In discussing little magnets we must not overlook the largest magnet of all—the earth itself. The earth is a powerful magnet and all magnets behave the same whether they be large or small. They attract iron and steel surely enough; and also magnets, under certain conditions, can push as hard as they can pull.

You should have four magnets and a cheap compass for the experiments about to be made. Two of the magnets should be shaped like horseshoes and two as plain bars of steel. Indeed, so-called permanent magnets are separated into only two classes: bar and horseshoe. (Magnetized steel in any form is usually called *permanently* magnetized although over a long period of time it will lose much of its power. If it is dropped a great deal or heated to a very high temperature, it quickly loses its power to attract.)

Great things have been happening with magnetism lately. A new kind of steel called Alnico (made of

A COMPASS, SIR, TO GUIDE YOU!

Asia, Alaska, or Death Valley? A compass will faithfully guide you home. Here we arrange a bar magnet at the North Pole of a globe. No matter where we put our compass thereafter, its busy finger will always point northward.

iron, carbon, aluminum, nickel and cobalt) has the old-fashioned magnetized steel beat all hollow. Magnets made of Alnico are very powerful devices. They will lift fifty times their own weight and are beautifully suited to the many fascinating and spectacular experiments to be made. While they cost a bit more than the ordinary steel magnets, they are worth more.

A few moments spent with two bar magnets, or two horseshoe magnets for that matter, can prove to be both edifying and highly interesting. One magnet is laid flat on the table; let's say one of the bar magnets. We approach it cautiously with a second magnet in our hand. Attraction, each for the other, does not necessarily follow. After all, magnets have *two different kinds of ends*, although they both appear identical. The ends of magnets are called *poles*. At one end there is the south pole and at the other end there is the north pole. Should it so happen that we bring the N pole of one magnet near the S pole of another, great attraction will result and the magnets will embrace each other. On the other hand, if the N pole of one magnet is brought near the N pole of another, great hostility between the two is instantly shown. The magnet on the table will demonstrate a really frantic effort to evade contact with the approaching magnet. It will indeed retreat as though it were actually alive and if we wish to bring the two N poles in actual contact, we shall have to grasp a magnet in each hand and *force* the two pole faces in contact.

From that experiment can be deduced a simple rule of magnetism that will be a guide in the experiments that follow. It is a simple rule. It states that like poles of magnets (as two N's or two S's) repel and that unlike poles (as an N and S) attract each other.

That is why a lodestone suspended on a thread

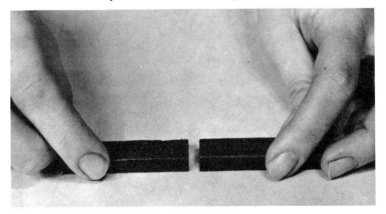

MAGNETS PUSH AS WELL AS PULL

Magnets not only embrace each other but also repel each other depending upon which ends are brought together. If they attract, it means S and N poles. If they repel, it is a case of N and N or S and S.

tends to point its end northward. The lodestone, too, has poles and its south pole is attracted to the earth's North Pole when it is not disturbed by other forces.

And why is the earth a magnet or, rather, why does the earth behave like a magnet? The answer is simple enough. The earth has in it great quantities of the metal iron and as much as one-eighth of its surface is composed of this useful material. Then, too, there is a certain amount of many other magnetic metals in the earth, principal among them, nickel and cobalt. All in all, they make of the earth a huge magnet.

We've already discovered a number of interesting and vital things that will prove immensely useful to us later on when we get down to serious business.

If we have that most valuable thing in the whole world, an inquiring mind, we shall want to learn more about the fundamental nature of this thing called magnetism. That we can do easily enough, although we can never hope actually to know what magnetism really is.

For the next piece of investigation, we shall need a teaspoonful of iron filings. Iron filings are not sold but they can be made with a file plus elbow grease. A medium-coarse file is used on a piece of soft iron held in a vise. If a power grinding wheel is near, then we shall have our teaspoonful of filings in no time. Of course, if one knows a man who works in a machine shop, he can get several teaspoonfuls from beneath the grinding wheel in the toolroom. For best results, the filings should be fine, and those from grinding wheels fill the bill perfectly.

Branching out from the pole faces or ends of every magnet are invisible tentacles, or what learned scientists call "magnetic lines of force." These lines of force have never been seen, of course, but we know that they exist because of the way iron filings act when they are exposed to heavy magnetic "fields." The filings snap to attention and line up. A remarkable little experiment will illustrate this. Simply place the iron filings on a piece of glass and hold the magnet underneath it. As we shall see when we conduct the experiment, the filings build up until the field or lines of force become so far removed from the poles of the magnet that they are no longer able to support the tiny particles of iron. From this we can certainly deduce that the force becomes weaker rapidly as the distance from the magnet is increased. We can put that down as a rule or law of magnetism.

FUZZY-WUZZY PICTURE OF A MAGNETIC FIELD

A magnet is laid underneath a piece of paper and iron filings from a salt shaker are sprinkled over it. The filings arrange themselves to conform to the magnetic pattern of the magnet.

The next experiment is both fascinating and highly instructive. The iron filings are placed in a salt shaker and carefully sprinkled as uniformly as possible over a piece of bristol board about 4 by 6 inches in size. Now we take our bar magnet, lay it on the table and carefully place the bristol board over it. Lo and behold! the iron particles immediately form a pattern; a magnetic pattern that will plot for us the shape and intensity of the mysterious force surrounding the magnet. We note with interest that at a point midway between the pole faces, the magnetic lines of force are weakest.

As we proceed, many questions will come begging for answers. For instance, we shall doubtlessly wonder what might happen if we cut a magnet in two. Would it lose its power or would we have two smaller and weaker magnets, each with its own N and S poles? To this the answer would be "Once a magnet, always a magnet." If a magnet were cut into a thousand pieces, there would be 1,000 N poles and 1,000 S poles.

Hundreds of delightfully instructive experiments

suggest themselves. If we are at all ingenious, we shall think of many things that are not suggested in this book. Countless hours may be whiled away. As an instance, one could place some iron filings in a phial and experiment with them for several hours. When the phial is placed on the poles or pole of a magnet, the phial may be lifted up and the tiny particles of

A MAGNETIC TEMPEST IN A BOTTLE

A small phial half-filled with iron filings offers a fascinating diversion. The mysterious magnetic force from a magnet penetrates the glass and does strange things to the contents.

iron will instantly rearrange themselves to conform to a magnetic pattern. Here we also learn that magnetism is capable of passing through matter; any kind of matter. If we try placing such things as wood, brass, zinc or copper between our magnet and the phial, we note that the magnetic force is still able to exert itself.

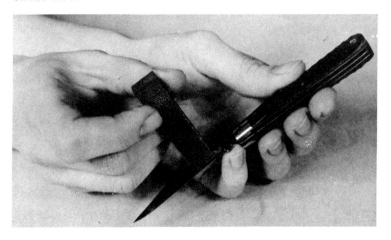

EVERY KNIFE A MAGNET WITH THIS TREATMENT

Magnetized pieces of steel can be used to magnetize other pieces of steel without losing their own power. Jack knife blades stroked with a magnet in *one direction only* become magnetized.

Strange and mysterious indeed is this thing called magnetism. Like radio, it can act across space. A needle left near or even brought near a magnet momentarily will become slightly magnetized. If it is permitted actually to touch a magnet, it will become quite heavily magnetized. We can easily magnetize the blades of our jackknife very substantially by merely stroking them *in one direction only and with one pole of the magnet only.* Thereafter, the blades

A JACK KNIFE BECOMES VERY ATTRACTIVE

This jack knife blade has been stroked by a magnet. Thereafter, it sets up shop for itself and is able to pick up and hold sizeable pieces of soft iron and steel.

will retain their power for a considerable period of time depending somewhat upon the quality of steel in them. We could magnetize a million blades in this simple fashion without our magnet losing one bit of its power. Wonderful? Yes, it is indeed. It is something like the laying on of magnetic hands that carry the power forward.

Magnetic lines of force are able to reach out over quite considerable distances. Men who work around heavy electrical machinery carry only the cheapest watches, because good watches made with high-quality steel would become so highly magnetized that they would no longer be able to keep accurate time.

If we wish to set our compass on a block of wood afloat in a dishpan full of water, we shall learn much about the function of marine compasses. Just to make the effect more marked, we shall dispense with reliance upon the earth's magnetic field and set up our own by the aid of two bar magnets. Here, however, we must be careful to see that the proper poles are used, one on each side of the pan. One must be an S and the other an N pole. We simply butt two magnets together and if the poles attract, we separate them and, holding the magnets in the same position, place one on one side of the pan and one on the other.

Now, the compass is placed on the "boat" and set adrift. We must make sure that the boat does not list so badly as to interfere with the movement of the compass needle which is delicately balanced on a pivot.

As we push the boat forward on the "ocean," it

THE SHIP THAT FLOATS IN A TIN PAN SEA

No romance of the Briny Deep here but plenty of elementary instruction in the use of the mariner's compass. Two bar magnets are arranged at either end of the "sea". No matter where the boat happens to be, the tell-tale needle points to the north.

will be noted that no matter where it is in the pan, the needle will always point north and south. Thus the mariner need only look at his compass to determine the direction in which his ship is headed in *relation* to the North Pole of the earth magnet.

In reality, of course, it is not quite as simple as that because the influence of the magnetic poles of the earth on compasses varies in different parts of the earth. However, mariners know what the variation amounts to and the necessary corrections corresponding to location may be made.

Many absorbing experiments with our earth as a magnet may be made even though it is very large. In one experiment, we magnetize a steel needle by stroking it with a bar magnet. This is then placed on a cork with a tiny drop of sealing wax and set adrift in a basin of water. If the cork is small enough and the needle magnetic enough, it will invariably point north and south if left to its own devices. It is as though some sort of a mysterious hand gently turned all tiny magnets so that they could pay their respects to the mother of all magnets, the earth itself.

A COMPASS ON A CORK

A magnetized darning needle, a large cork and a bit of sealing wax makes a sensitive and reliable compass. Left to its own devices on a quiet pool of water, it comes to rest pointing due north.

There is another form of magnetic needle that tells much about the secrets of the earth's magnetism. This is called an inclination or dip needle. Really it is very simple, but, like many seemingly simple things, quite wonderful. A reference to the photograph will show a crude homemade dip needle. It is mounted on sensitive pivot bearings just like a compass needle save that the needle operates in a vertical rather than a horizontal plane.

In one of our previous experiments, we discovered for ourselves that the magnetic field created by a magnet is not uniform. It is strongest at the poles and weakest in the exact center. There is no reason why the earth should be any exception to this rule and the magnetic dip needle proves indeed that it is not. As

THE DIP NEEDLE MEASURES MAGNETISM

The earth is a huge magnet with North and South poles. Magnetism varies between maximum at the poles and minimum at the equator. At the poles this needle would dip most. At the equator it would not dip at all.

in the case of the mariner's compass or any compass for that matter, the needle of the inclination compass is a small piece of highly magnetized steel. When properly mounted, this needle should be carefully balanced so as to tend to remain in a normally horizontal position. Its departure from this position will depend entirely upon where it is on the surface of the earth. If it is in Singapore, it will dip less than it will in Alaska. Indeed if we traveled over the entire surface of the earth with this instrument and took readings in each place visited, we could develop a chart which would clearly show the nature, size and intensity of the earth's magnetic field. There is little need of doing this, however, for scientists have already traveled enough with inclination needles to be pretty sure that mother earth is a very ordinary kind of magnet. If we were at either the North Pole or the South Pole, either one or the other end of the inclination needle would go straight down. On the other hand, if we traveled to the center of the earth on the equator, there would be no dip whatsoever.

It is really amazing the fun that may be had with

a small magnet (especially of the bar type) and a cheap compass such as is used by the Boy Scouts. For instance, place the compass on a table and keep a watchful eye on it as you move about the room with the magnet in your hand. Perhaps you will be surprised to note that the needle of the compass will faithfully follow your movements.

The experimenter new to this business of magnetism may well ask why it is that the compass obeys the local magnet rather than the magnetic influence of the earth. The answer is very simple. The local magnet, because of its proximity to the compass, exerts a more powerful influence on it and overpowers the earth magnet. After all, it is but a few inches away while the magnetic poles of the earth may be 5,000 miles away. Mother Earth is a powerful magnet, but not quite that powerful!

Let us now try another experiment. Leaving the compass on the table, point one pole of the bar magnet at it from a distance of, say, six inches. Instantly, the little needle will point at the magnet. Now, without changing the location of the compass, turn the bar magnet around, keeping a weather eye on the compass needle. Surely enough it, too, turns as though a spirit hand had so willed. No matter how quickly we manipulate the bar magnet, the little compass needle will not be far behind. Why?

Well, we have already learned that like poles of magnets such as two souths are hostile to each other and exert repulsion rather than the attraction that is normally associated with magnetism. Hence, if the south pole of the magnet is pointed toward the compass needle, the north pole of the needle will be attracted. A mere vice versa supplies the rest of the answer.

So much for an introduction to the marvelous science of magnetism. After all, it is by no means the dull subject that many think it to be. Hundreds of exciting experiments beckon us and so we turn to fresh pages for more adventure in the mysterious realm of a truly mysterious force.

Chapter 2

BIG STUNTS WITH LITTLE MAGNETS

No matter what we might do, we cannot avoid moving about through the ever-present, invisible magnetic lines of force that constantly wash over the face of the earth. Although we are not in any sense conscious of it, we live in a great magnetic field. It pervades our bodies at all times, the lines of force passing through us as easily as they pass through paper, glass or air.

Powerful magnets, either small or large, behave strangely toward each other. Either they fondly embrace or violently reject each other when brought close together. The effects can be studied with sen-

23

sational results if we have at hand two small bar magnets of the Alnico type. One is laid on the table and the second one, held parallel, is placed over it. If the two magnets are so held that their respective poles are opposite each other, they will snap together with a loud click. If, on the other hand, the poles are opposed, we shall feel a strong cushioning effect as we bring the magnet in the hand near the one on the table. It is almost as though some sort of invisible spring were present between the two. We push down and feel a counterforce pushing back. It is indeed very uncanny; almost spooky! Of course, if we do not take care, the magnet underneath will quickly turn and align its poles with the upper magnet for sympathetic attraction. Evidently, magnets don't really relish being hostile to each other.

For the next experiment, we bring either the two N or the two S poles together, each magnet lying flat on the table. When they are in actual contact, we quickly withdraw our hand. The magnets instantly snap apart. It is as though an invisible spring between them had been compressed. Here we are dealing with

A MAGNETIC ACROBAT

Two horseshoe magnets are brought into positions where they oppose each other; that is N to N and S to S. They are then placed on the table and held as above. When the fingers are removed, the top magnet will leap into the air.

a force that was perhaps just as confusing to Dr. Albert Einstein as it is to us, rank novices that we are.

You can have lots of fun with steel balls. Perhaps a trip to the local auto junk yard will bring an old ball bearing for the asking. It does not have to be a good one for you merely take it apart for the steel balls.

Next, mount a piece of glass in a wooden frame or use a small picture frame after removing the back and

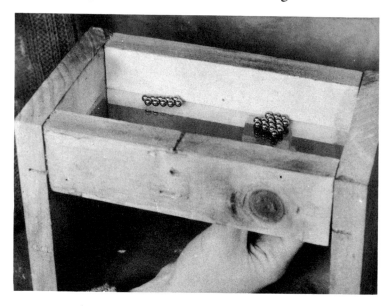

FUN WITH STEEL BALLS

Steel balls taken from ball bearings will become highly active on a smooth glass surface. They also become magnetized when exposed to other magnets. Thereafter, by the use of a magnet underneath the glass, much fun may be had by the formation of various patterns, etc.

the picture. What you need is a horizontal glass surface over which the steel balls may frolic without danger of losing them. They must be fenced in, so to speak. The simple device shown in the photo is ideal because it is provided with legs.

So equipped, set the steel balls free on the glass surface and operate the magnet from beneath. One would have to be dull-witted indeed not to enjoy an hour or so with this simple arrangement. Like a flock of magnetic sheep, the little steel balls scurry about the glass surface, following the magnet. The balls, too, become magnetized, each with its N and S poles. After this happens, their movements and behavior are not so easy to predict but that adds to the fun.

A slot sawed in a piece of wood provides all the equipment needed for another interesting diversion with the steel balls. They are lined up in the slot like a bunch of magnetic soldiers. By this time, each ball carries a considerable amount of magnetism and, although you will not notice it as it happens, each soldier will come to rest with his N pole next to his neighbor's S pole.

Once the soldiers are "at attention," approach the last one with the magnet. Sheeplike or perhaps soldier-like, they all follow and, if you proceed cautiously, a large number of the steel balls may be picked up to form a string of magnetic beads. (See frontispiece.)

How would you like to make some South Sea Island Magnetic Bugs? First, go to a drugstore and ask the druggist for a half-dozen capsules about 1 inch long. Then color or stain the insides of the capsules to prevent an examination of the contents. This can be done with red or black ink or with the fine aluminum powder that comes with the aluminum paint sold in the five-and-ten-cent stores.

After the interior of each capsule has been colored, slip a steel ball into each one and put the cover in place. And so the South Sea Island Magnetic Bugs are born as we shall see. Several of them are placed on a heavy piece of cardboard. A magnet is then placed beneath the cardboard. Instantly the Bugs jump into a frenzy of motion especially if the magnet continues to move. Naturally, the little steel balls inside the capsules are free to move about within limits and such

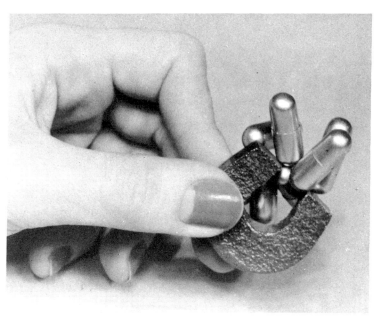

THESE STRANGE SOUTH SEA ISLAND
MAGNETIC BUGS

A ball bearing in a capsule makes a lively magnetic bug,
strangest of all creatures. The free movement of the steel
balls within the capsules brings weird results.

movements produce curious and humorous movements on the part of the capsules. Talk about Mexi-
can Jumping Beans! They are quite tame by com-
parison. When the ball within a capsule moves from
one end to another under the influence of the mag-

net, the capsule becomes bottom heavy and it stands on end. Not only that, but it moves end over end as the magnet underneath the cardboard is moved backward and forward. The capsules behave as though they are alive and you can have a circus with them.

There is a fascinating game that can be played with

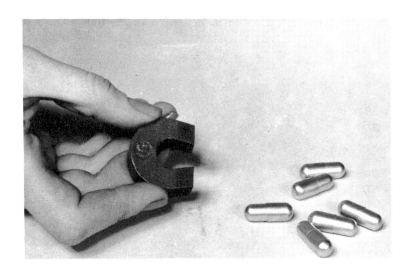

THE MAGNETIC CALL OF THE WILD

When a strong magnet is brought near the South Sea Island Magnetic Bugs, there is a curious stirring and then a lively movement, end on end, toward the mother magnet.

these South Sea Island Magnetic Bugs. We take a piece of wall board about 18 inches square and cut a 2-inch round hole in the exact center. Then the board is provided with legs just high enough to permit us to place our hand under it — say 6 inches high. Each player is given three "bugs" and the first to dump his bugs in the hole wins the game. All movements must be conducted by the aid of the magnet in the hand working from beneath. If one player sees that his opponent is about to deposit a bug in the hole, he is free to interfere with his magnet to prevent the action. The erratic and at times unpredictable movement of the insects makes the game a very exciting one even for the spectators.

There is a magnetic version of "Pick-up-Sticks" that is interesting. Tenpenny nails are used and they are laid side by side on a board that has been ruled off in spaces ½ inch wide. Each nail is laid as close to the center of each space as possible. The trick is that of removing one nail at a time with the magnet without in the least disturbing adjacent nails. It can be done but not as easily as one might think. Some prac-

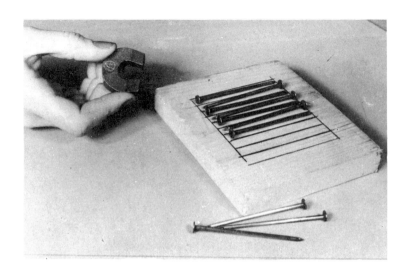

MAGNETIC "PICK-UP STICKS"

If you have a steady hand and a good nervous system, you win. The stunt calls for the removal of each nail without disturbing, even slightly, the remaining nails. It's not an easy trick; just hard enough to challenge one.

tice is required although an unusually skillful person might accomplish the feat after the second or third trial.

Another version of the same stunt is shown in the photograph. Here nine nails are stood on end and separated by only ½ inch. It will be found that box nails are ideal for this purpose because of their large heads. The trick, again, is that of removing all of the nails, one at a time, without dislocating adjacent nails. Here indeed is a severe test for frayed nerves.

Those who like puzzle stunts of this sort will also be interested in the ball-bearing trick. A slot is sawed lengthwise in a board and spaces ¼ inch apart are ruled off as clearly shown in the photograph. Care-

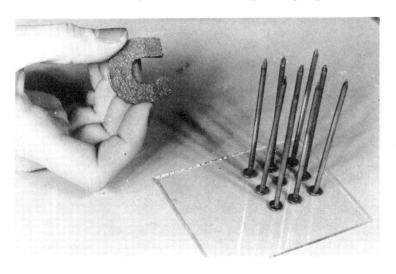

STEP FORWARD, SIR!

Here's a squad of nails under the command of a magnetic sergeant. One by one he calls them forth but, as he does, those which remain must stand perfectly still.

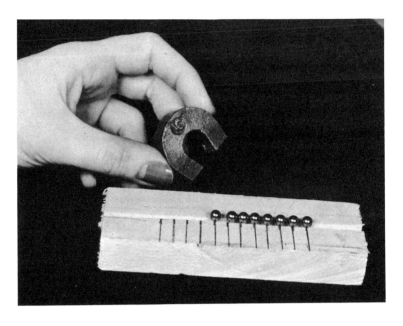

ANOTHER CHALLENGE TO STEADY HANDS

These ball bearings are separated by only a quarter of an inch. Armed only with a small but powerful magnet, one must coax away one bearing at a time. It's not easy but it is fun and it can be done.

fully the ball bearings are lined up ¼ inch apart with the aid of the ruled lines. Now grasp the magnet firmly and set forth to coax away one ball at a time. If you so much as disturb an adjacent ball, the jig is up; you are defeated. The trick can be accomplished

surely enough with practice but the secret will not
be divulged. It is better to develop your own skills.
After the secret is known, it will be fun indeed to
watch our friends try to solve the problem.

The trick to be described next is indeed the magnetic trick of tricks. It is baffling and utterly fascinating. To practice it we mount twenty ¾-inch iron

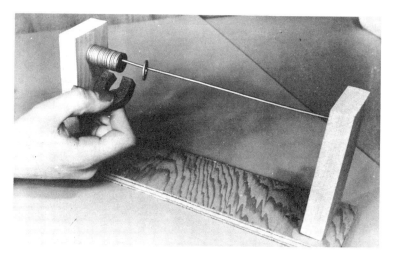

MOVE NO MORE THAN ONE AT A TIME, PLEASE

Here is a fascinating puzzle in magnetism. The trick is to
move one washer at a time without in the least disturbing
the remainder. The text tells the tale. It can be done.

washers on a heavy steel wire as illustrated. The washers are then pushed back to one end of the rack until they are all closely packed together. It will challenge our ingenuity to coax away one washer at a time armed only with a horseshoe magnet. Can one actually bring the magnet in contact with a washer? Yes, indeed, but this will defeat rather than assist the operation.

Unless one had done considerable experimenting, it is questionable whether the trick could be discovered. Here the difficulties are such that directions are in order.

First, it is vital that the magnet be held in the hand exactly as illustrated; that is, horizontally. The distance between the magnet and the washer to be removed by magnetic persuasion, should not exceed 1 inch. With the magnet so held and with the distance so adjusted, the hand is moved rapidly back and forth. Strangely enough, and for reasons not clearly understood, this action will peel off one washer at a time. Of course, after a washer has been separated from the group in this way, it is a very easy matter to butt up

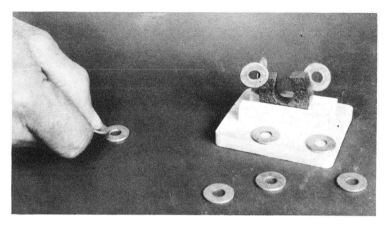

PLAY A GAME OF MAGNETIC TIDDLY WINKS

A modern version of a very old game. In place of the cup
to catch the winks, a magnet is used to catch iron washers,
if one is clever enough to shoot them in the right direction.
The player who lands all of his winks on the magnet first
wins.

to it with the magnet and violently carry it away.

Tiddly winks was quite a game when we were
very young. It was played with some large and small
buttons and a cup. A large button held in the hand was
pressed against the small buttons lying on the table in
such a way as to flip them through the air into the cup.
The winner was the one who succeeded in placing
all his buttons in the cup first.

There is a neat magnetic version of this game. First,

we mount a horseshoe magnet on a board so that its pole faces are upward. We then cut a 12-inch circle or disk from bristol board and place the magnet directly in the center of this. Each player is given an equal number of ¾-inch iron washers: his winks. Shooting from outside the boundary established by the bristol board disk, the player who first succeeds in making all his washers stick to the magnet wins. Either that or the one who succeeds in making the larger number stick from say a supply of half a dozen. Unless a very large and powerful magnet is employed, only a few washers should be used by each of the players. And those who don't think the game is real fun should try it. For best results, the winks should be snapped on a hard surface covered with two layers of medium-heavy cloth.

Locomotion is easily produced by the aid of magnets. To make a stunt of it, we saw two grooves in a board 18 inches long. The grooves should not be less than ⅜ of an inch deep and ⅛ of an inch from the edge of the board. Also, the grooves should be wide enough to accommodate the iron washers we have been using. By wide enough, we mean with enough width to spare, so that the washer will be free to roll in the groove.

Each opponent in the contest has a washer and each washer is placed at a starting line at the end of the board. Upon a given signal, the contestants use

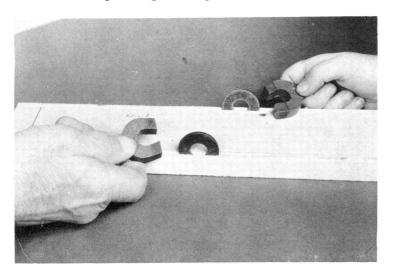

THE RACE OF THE MAGNETIC WASHERS

Here each contestant has a magnet and a washer that can move along in a groove. The players are not permitted to touch their "racers" with the magnet but must coax them along without contact of any kind.

their magnets only to move the washers along in the grooves. No actual contact is permitted. If it comes about accidentally, disqualification results and the race goes to the opponent.

Of course, the closer the magnet is held to the washer, the greater the possibilities for speed. On the other hand, there is also the constant danger that the washer will suddenly fly to the magnet and disqualify the overanxious player. It is the temptation to produce the highest speed that helps to make the game real fun. However, an observant player will soon discover the correct distance between the magnet and the washer. After that he will astound his less skillful opponents.

Here is a bottle trick that will keep the boys and girls interested and busy for a spell. The success of the stunt depends almost entirely upon the shape of the bottle you use. The type shown is just right. The shoulders of the bottle are all important. They must not be too sloping and they must not be too abrupt. In the first case the trick would be far too simple and in the second case it could not be worked at all. The bot-

MAGNETIC RESCUE FROM A BOTTLE

Here is a "party stunt" worth remembering. The contestants
see who can remove a sheet steel object from a glass bottle in
the shortest time. Those who try to move the steel article too
fast will drop it and have to start all over again.

tle shown is the half-gallon kind used for distilled
water.

Inside this bottle we place some sort of light, magnetically responsive article like the sheet iron screw
cap from a bottle. Brass or aluminum caps, obviously,
will not do. Once the piece is inside the bottle, we

are required to remove it with the use of nothing but the magnet. Here the novice will defeat himself in a number of easy ways. First he will try to move the article too fast. If this is done the magnet will not be able to carry it along and it will fall to the bottom of the bottle. At any rate, it is a good stunt and lots of fun can be had working at it.

Chapter 3

MAGNETS THAT FLOAT IN THE AIR

WHILE, as we have seen, all magnets can be made to repel each other under prescribed circumstances, some magnets made of the more common steels do not exert enough repulsive force to be noticeable. For the purposes at hand, we shall need a few of the newer and more powerful Alnico magnets either of the small horseshoe or bar type or both. Not only do such magnets demonstrate attraction with greater force but repulsion as well, as we shall presently see.

"Like poles of magnets repel each other and unlike poles attract each other." No one in the whole world can really tell us just what the nature of this force is.

When the N poles of two Alnico magnets are brought together, there appears to be an invisible cushion between them. It is a weird, mysterious effect. If we do not hold them tightly when this is done, they will twist and squirm to readjust themselves in such a manner that they can embrace each other with their N and S poles in opposition. This is beautifully demonstrated in the simple experiment shown in the photograph on page 25. Making sure that the N pole of one magnet is placed on top of the N pole of another, we hold the top magnet in place with our fingers. We then suddenly lift the fingers to leave the magnets to their own devices. The response is quick and invariably the same. The top magnet will actually leap an inch or so into the air, do a complete turn and come down with its poles reversed, and the magnets will come together with a sharp click. Nature cleverly conceals her methods but her effects are there for all to see and admire.

There is another experiment in magnetic repulsion

that is amusing. For this it will be necessary to set up a wooden track or a set of wooden guide rails placed such a distance apart that the magnets we have will be able to slide along without being able to turn around. The photograph shows the simple device clearly enough. Horseshoe magnets will usually be longer than they are wide which would prevent them from twisting too far.

The magnets are arranged face-to-face as illustrated but here we must take care to see that their polarities are arranged for repulsion rather than attraction. A brief test will determine this. If the magnets attract each other when so arranged, then we simply reverse one — that is, turn it over — to insure the opposite effect.

So arranged, one magnet will be pushed ahead of the other without material contact. The effect is rather startling to uninformed people who have always associated magnetism with attraction. Yet the magnets stubbornly refuse to embrace each other and actual force will have to be brought to bear upon them before they can be brought into contact. Im-

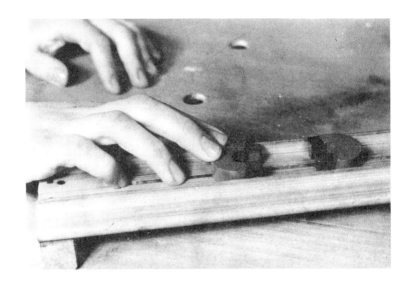

ONE MAGNET "CHASES" ANOTHER

The repulsion between Alnico magnets is so great that when
they are prevented from twisting as shown, one can be used
to push the other without contact. Here, as in all cases of repulsion, the N poles and S poles oppose each other.

mediately this force is removed, the invisible "spring"
that exists between the pole faces will come into
action and the magnets will fly apart covering a distance often running as great as several inches. Of
course, here we must bear in mind that the violence
of the action will depend a great deal upon the power

of the magnets employed. Weak magnets of the old type, that is magnets of ordinary grades of steel, will not exhibit the effect to any noticeable extent. On the other hand, "fresh" magnets of the Alnico type will amaze and thrill us with their active response.

This repulsion between magnets of the Alnico type can be made much more convincing by the demonstration of actual levitation; that is the actual support of one magnet by another in mid-air and without material contact. It is an amazing sight. As in previous cases, we simply must see to it that our magnets are made to behave properly. Left to their own devices, they fail to demonstrate levitation or suspension because they will twist and squirm until they bring themselves into the alignment necessary for attraction which is their normal tendency. Hence, we must build some sort of simple framework which will not interfere with the upward or vertical movements of the top magnet but which will effectively prevent the twisting or turning of either one of the magnets used. Of course, the actual construction and design of this simple equipment will depend largely upon the type of magnets we are using, whether they are bar or horseshoe. To meet either situation, we have presented here the details of a rack or frame for either kind of magnet.

The rack needed for Alnico bar magnets simply amounts to a series of brass or wooden pegs driven into a small board. The photograph will greatly clarify the construction details. We say either brass or wood because these materials are nonmagnetic. It would, of course, be easiest to use nails, but nails, because of their high response to magnetic forces, would ruin the experiment entirely. If we want to use wood, ¼-inch dowels can be employed, or even match sticks for that matter. In such a case, we would simply drill a few holes in the baseboard of the device and set the matches in these, smearing the end of each one with a bit of glue. If ⅛-inch brass rods are used for the guideposts, the holes should have a diameter of slightly under ⅛ inch so that the rods can be forced into place.

One magnet is placed at the bottom of the rack. Then the other magnet is placed over it and, if the

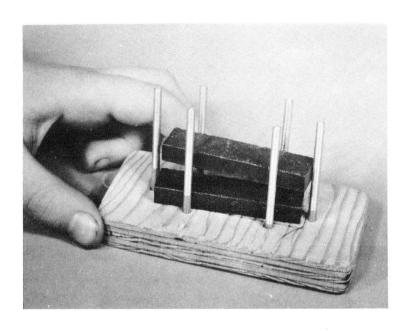

A MAGNET THAT "FLOATS ON AIR"

Really this magnet does not "float on air". It is being held above the bottom magnet by magnetic forces alone. The metal pegs driven into the board are for the purpose of preventing the magnets from twisting about to a position of mutual attraction.

polar relationship is properly arranged, the second magnet will refuse to rest on the first one. Rather it will remain suspended in the air above the bottom magnet. If we press it with our finger and force it down into contact with the lower magnet, it will instantly spring upward when the finger is withdrawn. As we press downward, we can feel a force pushing upward that is much like that produced by a spring on a soft piece of rubber. Here we are face to face with one of the major mysteries of the universe. We know little or nothing about the real or ultimate nature of magnetism, but we do know that it is most intimately associated with the structure of matter.

If our magnets are of the horseshoe type, then we shall have to make other arrangements for the experiment. Another photograph shows a rack or frame intended for use with magnets of this kind. Here two wooden uprights are employed and these are nailed to a small baseboard. The distance between them must be adjusted to accommodate the magnets at hand. The magnets should just fit in between the uprights, perhaps a little tightly.

After the first magnet is in place, a small piece of wood must be wedged into the framework in such a way that it will come between the poles of the bottom magnet and the top magnet.

MAGNETIC LEVITATION BY REPULSION

In this case, one magnet is suspended over another so that the
N poles and the S poles are opposed. Under such conditions,
the repulsion will be so great, that the top magnet will remain
literally floating on the air. The frame merely prevents the
twisting of the magnets.

(If one has enough magnets to devote one of them to this experiment exclusively, the piece of wood can be glued into place permanently.) If this precaution is not taken, then no levitation will take place, because the N pole of one of the magnets will slip through the framework over to the S pole of the other magnet, and attraction will result.

Now when the second magnet is slipped in place over the bottom one it will remain suspended for an indefinite period. The experimenter must recall, however, that this matter of suspension can be demonstrated only by highly magnetized Alnico magnets. Magnets made of ordinary steel will not be powerful enough to produce suspension or levitation of any kind.

There is another and still more spectacular experiment in levitation shown in the accompanying photograph. In this, one magnet is held down permanently on a small wooden pedestal and the other magnet "floats" in midair, being prevented from making contact with the first by two pieces of string. This time levitation is produced by attraction and

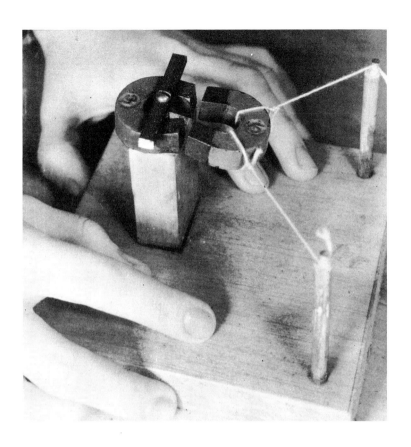

MAGNETIC LEVITATION WITH A VENGEANCE

We see here a magnet actually "floating" on air with nothing to hold it but two pieces of string. This beautiful experiment will never fail to puzzle your friends and fascinate them. When so suspended, the magnet will bear up under consider-able pressure before it will fall.

not by means of repulsion as was the case in our previous experiment.

The apparatus we have just been discussing is simple enough but it will be necessary to adjust the length of the pieces of string so as to prevent actual contact of the pole faces of the magnets.

Chapter 4

TOYS THAT MOVE WITH MAGNETISM

THE amazing power of the Alnico magnets makes them useful for many things for which the older types of magnet could not be used with any degree of success. For one thing, the new magnets can be used to power certain toys that lend themselves perfectly to magnetic control. As an example, take small automobiles such as may be purchased for ten cents or so in the chain stores. Then there are simple wooden boats which you can make yourself. Simply place a piece of soft iron, which may be all or part of a large nail, underneath the boat or automobile and then use a magnet to control its movements. The boats will appear to move under their own power as though some little Diesel engine were tucked away in their hulls. The automobiles, too, will act as though they had a tiny engine under their hoods.

Let's take up the matter of the automobiles first. We must make sure that the cars are not too heavy. If they are too heavy for the magnets we have, they will either not respond at all or very sluggishly. Sluggish action will take away most of the fun. But we can go to the local chain stores in search of small, light, plastic automobiles; something about 2 ½ inches long.

Next, we must prepare the car for magnetic locomotion. This is done simply enough. Of course, it is best to place a good-sized piece of soft iron underneath the car so that the magnet can get a good "grip." On the other hand, we do not want to attach a piece of iron so heavy that it will "stall" the car and prevent it from moving at all. A piece of strap iron about ⅛ of an inch thick and ½ inch wide is just about right. Its length should amount to the width of the car itself.

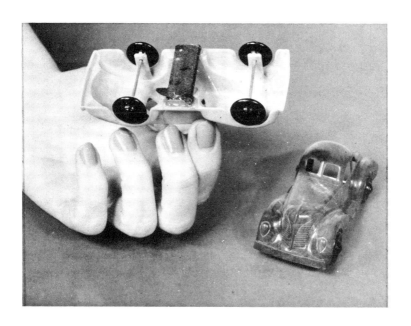

PREPARING CARS FOR MAGNETIC POWER

These light plastic cars are made ready for magnetic power
by cementing a small piece of soft iron to their undersides.
The wheels should be treated with light oil to make them
roll more easily.

This piece of soft iron must be attached to the bottom of the car to be moved. It can either be wired in place or held with household cement. Ordinary glue will not do the job except in a very precarious manner. Perhaps our preparation of the tiny automobiles should also include oiling the wheels with a very thin lubricant. The more easily the little cars move about the better.

Our magnet used for locomotion will perhaps perform its duties better if we attach it to the end of a

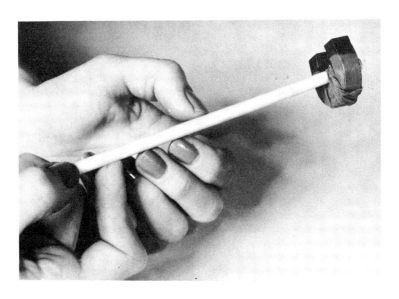

MAGNETIC POWER AT THE END OF A STICK

A small magnet held to the end of a piece of doweling by means of rubber bands will be a great help in guiding boats and automobiles with magnetic power. The piece of doweling should be about 14 inches long.

small wooden dowel or stick with a rubber band. In the case of running one of our cars down the streets of Model Town, we shall not have to stretch our arm.

The simple operation of the magnetically controlled car is shown in one of the photographs where it is passing along a street lined with model houses. Here we have a high degree of realism.

The "street" can be either heavy cardboard or the thinnest kind of plywood you can buy at the lumber

A CAR MOVES ALONG "MAGNETIC AVENUE"

A surprising degree of control can be exercised over these model cars by means of the magnet underneath the surface of the "street". The cars used should be as light as possible.

yard. Of course the automobile will work much better and move much faster if a thin material is used. Anything as thick as ½ inch or more will place serious obstacles in our way. When the magnetic lines of force have to pass through things that are too thick, a great deal of their strength is lost.

If we have a few pasteboard model houses, so much the better. These can be arranged as shown for a "street" and magnetically operated cars can run up and down. Indeed, you can even practice traffic rules here.

Next come mysterious ships that sail under "magnetic orders"! Take a small wooden boat, one not over 3 inches long. Here again guard against too much weight. The little boat must be propelled by magnetism that comes up through the bottom of a pan and a certain amount of water.

If you make a boat, cut it from a solid piece of soft pine. Use a solid piece of soft pine because such wood cuts easily, and because laminated wood, such as plywood, is easily affected by the water and comes apart. Any kind of boat may be chosen although the freighter shown in the photograph offers a most interesting type. Then you might like a tugboat to go with it.

A FREIGHTER WITH A MAGNETIC MOTOR

This boat measures three inches in length and the hull is cut from a piece of soft pine. A two-inch nail is cemented to the bottom of the craft for the purpose of magnetic control.

If you want to make a "shore" for this magnetic sea that we are to build, this "shore" or "land" can be cut from any sort of boxwood. It may help if you cover both it and the boats with a single coat of shellac. This is for protection from the action of the water. After the shellac has dried, the boats may be painted any color desired. Perhaps a little brown or green paint on the "land" might also help.

If the builder would like to have a lighthouse, the tower is easily cut from a broomstick or mop handle. The window and door can be drawn with ink. This,

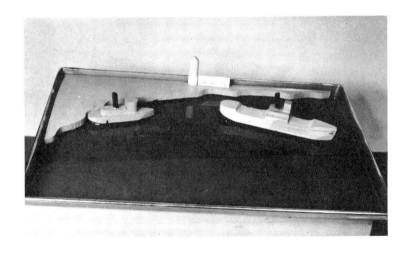

SHIPS THAT SAIL MAGNETIC SEAS

These two boats can be controlled perfectly by moving a magnet about underneath the pan, which happens to be an aluminum cookie tray. The tray can be of any non-magnetic metal.

together with the house associated with it, is cemented to the "land" near the shore of the sea.

The pan for the water requires some thought, for it has to be just the right kind of pan. Certainly it must be fairly large. Otherwise our fleet will be pretty cramped and we shall not be able to maneuver our boats very well. On the other hand, we should remember, too, that it might not be wise to employ a sheet iron or sheet steel because magnetism passes through such metals very poorly. By the time it passes through even a thin sheet of such material, a great deal of its strength disappears. Aluminum, copper or brass pans are suitable, but the best one to use is a large, shallow aluminum one. It's a good idea to paint the bottom and sides a sea green.

Cement a small nail to the bottom of each boat, as near the center as possible. Although it is not positively necessary, we will do a better job if we cut a groove in the boat into which the nail may be fitted. In any event, the nail is placed on the bottom of the boat and then smothered with household cement to hold it in place. If the boat lists a bit after it has been

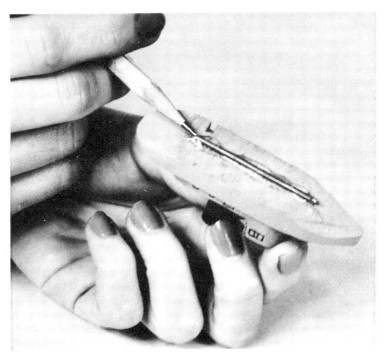

A "MOTOR" FOR MAGNETIC BOATS

A nail is attached to the bottom of each boat by means of household cement. Better results are had if a groove is provided for the nail. Care should also be taken to see that the nail is mounted in the exact center of the craft.

placed in the water, readjust it either by shaving off a bit of wood or placing a tiny weight on the side opposite the list.

When the boats are ready, place them in the pan and hold the magnet underneath it. The boat nearest the magnet responds instantly and off it goes. There is a distinct limit to the speed that can be attained, of course; if you move the magnet too fast, the boats will simply be left behind.

You can make fish which can be controlled the same way as are the boats and automobiles. For materials, you need some ¼-inch thick boxwood. On this draw pictures of the kind of fish you want. Practically every dictionary has a page full of pictures of fish, in natural colors. The fish should be about 2 inches long.

After they are drawn on the wood, cut them out with a scroll saw. Perhaps a little dressing up with a bit of sandpaper would help. If they are painted, so much the better. However, before this is done, cut a slit or groove in the bottom of the fish; that is, the edge that swims downward. Into this wedge a small piece of soft sheet iron or a piece of sheet tin plate, which can be cut from a tin can. This is the magnetic element that must be carried by the fish if they are going to move about on the "sea."

If, after the fish is in the water, it pitches forward or backward, then adjust the position of the piece of sheet steel accordingly. If the pitch is forward, move the steel in the groove toward the tail of the fish.

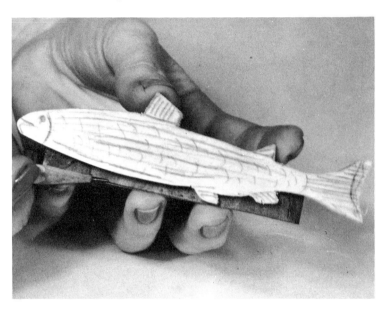

FISH, TOO, CAN BE MADE MAGNETIC

A slit is cut in the belly of a wooden fish and a small piece of sheet iron is pressed into place. Thereafter, the fish can be made to swim under perfect magnetic control.

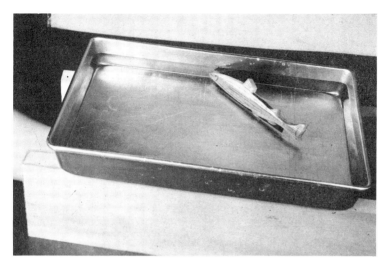

THIS FISH SWIMS IN A STRANGE SEA

This magnetically controlled fish can be made to swim at any level depending upon how far or how near to the bottom of the pan the magnet is held.

As you use these magnetic fish, you will find that a fine degree of control can be exercised over them. Not only can you make the fish swim from place to place in the pool but you can also make them swim at any level you wish. For instance, if you bring your magnet in contact with the bottom of the pan, the fish will be unable to resist the magnetic field and it will be powerful enough to bring them directly to the bottom of the water. As you move the magnet away from the bottom of the pan, the fish will rise and you can even let them go back to the surface, where you will still be able to exercise control over them.

Chapter 5

MAKE THESE GAMES WITH MAGNETS!

M AGNETISM offers us many different ways to fun
and instruction. If we are at all clever and
thoughtful, we can devise many simple games that can
be played by the aid of one or two common horseshoe
or bar magnets. Just to show how easy it is to do this,
we start the ball rolling with a few suggestions. The
games about to be described involve only the simplest
kinds of materials, they require no skill to make and
actual use will soon prove that boys and girls may
have a circus with them.

One of the games has two goals. For this reason,

we can call it Magnetic Hockey or Magnetic Football. If we are football fans, then it is football.

As will be noticed in the accompanying photograph, the game board itself is very simple. It can be cut from thin plywood and it is ruled off in seven sections. However, you can use any number of sections that you wish. The board itself measures 18 by 18 inches and the two end zones, where the goals are located, are painted a different color from the center or playing area of the board. The color will depend upon your choice or whatever paint or enamel happens to be at hand.

Within these end zones place two goals; these are formed with small pieces of wood about ¼ inch square. They are nailed or glued into place to form an enclosure 2 inches wide and 5 inches long.

The playing board will have to be elevated about 5 to 7 inches so that you can get your hand underneath it. As a matter of fact, it is strictly against the rules to withdraw the hand during actual play. The game is played by means of magnets. All the movements of the football (or the puck) must

MAGNETIC FOOTBALL IS FUN TO PLAY

A sheet steel screw cap from a bottle is here used as a football
the movements of which are controlled from underneath the
board by a magnet in the hand of each player. The players
protect their goal zones as best they can.

be brought about by the use of the magnet alone. It
is also against the rules to move the playboard while
the game is on. Such movements cost a goal.

To play this game, take a small sheet steel screw
cap from some sort of bottle. Be sure, however, that
the cap is not aluminum or brass. A slight scratch

made with a knife will soon reveal whether you have the right kind. This cap serves as the ball or puck.

To start the game, the bottle cap is placed in the center of the board. Each contestant, magnet ready, places his hand at the rear edge of his goal. When the signal to start is given, the contestants move their magnets under the board and toward the ball or puck as quickly as possible. Each tries to gain control over the movements of the bottle cap. Actual pushing is not permissible because then the winner of the game would simply be the stronger of the two players and this would not be fair. That is not the object of the game at all. The object is to see who is the most skillful in moving the football or puck into his opponent's goal.

Merely reading about this game does not do it justice. A barrel of fun can be had with it. Even older people have been known to sit down with this and enjoy themselves for an hour or more. The fun comes mostly because of the rather unpredictable movements of the "football." It does not by any means always perform as the players wish. For one thing, each player is very apt to become too anxious to move it and try to produce too much speed. When this happens, that is, when he moves his magnet too fast, he will lose the "ball." There is a distinct limit to the speed of its motion.

Perhaps the players will wish to formulate their own rules for actual play. There are several ways of keeping score. The best allots a certain time for play, say ten minutes, and at the end of this time, the winner is the one who has scored the most goals.

There is another goal game that offers loads of fun and this, too, is very simply made. Although the court can easily be made with plywood, there is no reason why an ordinary household tray cannot be used for the purpose. Here the ball is actually a ball, a ping-pong ball. Of course, ping-pong balls, as they come from the store, are not magnetic in any sense of the word and, furthermore, they cannot be influenced by magnets. There is a way of treating them, however, so that they will respond to magnets. To bring this about, take a sharp knife and cut a tiny slit about ½ inch long in the ball. Carefully prying this slit open with the blade of the knife in such a way as not to break the ball, drop one of your steel balls in the opening. After the blade of the knife has been withdrawn, the slit in the ping-pong ball will close. Then, of course, the ping-pong ball will respond to the magnet. The little steel ball inside the big ball will be attracted by the magnet and this, due to the lightness of the ping-pong ball, will cause the ping-pong ball to roll along but in the most awkward and humorous way. It really waggles and staggers and its movements are extremely difficult to predict.

For the goals of this game, use two magnets placed back to back as shown in the photograph. They are laid as close to the center of the enclosed court as possible. Perhaps it would be wise to mark off a small square in the center of the court to indicate the position of the magnets.

There is a magnet goal for each player; one for A and one for B. The movement of the ball must be controlled only by blowing through a straw. If B succeeds in driving the ball to A's magnet and making it stick there, then B has scored a point. Naturally

STRAWS ARE USED TO PLAY THIS GAME

Here two magnets are placed in the center of the playing
court and the ping-pong ball is blown about by the opponents. Each has a magnetic goal that will attract the ball and
each tries to prevent the ball from reaching his own goal.

each player tries hard not only to guard his own goal
but to drive the ball to his opponent's goal. The magnets bring about a form of dynamic action that is most
interesting because it is at times so cantankerous. The
game itself proves to be utterly fascinating.

There is another game that you can make using
the same ping-pong ball. When you tire of playing

ne where the loaded ping-pong ball is blown
d with the soda straws, you can build the device
sh. n below. Here the ball is suspended by a thread

THE MAGNETIC PING-PONG BALL

The ping-pong ball is made to respond magnetically by cutting a small slit in it and inserting a steel ball. The game is
played as described in the text.

from a wooden standard. The thread is attached both to the standard and to the ball by means of household cement. The standard and the string should be just long enough (and no longer) to permit either one of the magnets shown to catch and hold the ping-pong ball.

Here again the game is played with soda straws, the contestants attempting to fasten the ball onto their opponent's magnetic goal post. This counts a point each time.

Almost every boy and girl has some kind of game that uses a spinner. By a spinner, we mean a numbered dial with a needle mounted on it, the spinning of which determines the number of moves or plays to be made in a game. This little device can also be used to play a game if we make use of our magnets. For this game, divide the spinner card into two halves. Each player tries with his magnet to make the pointer of the needle stop on his half of the card. Say he makes the pointer stop on the segment marked 5. He then adds five to his score. He cannot, however, interfere with the movement of the needle in any way except

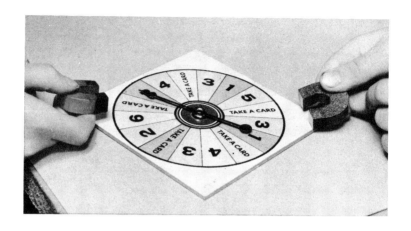

THE GAME SPINNER OBEYS THE MAGNETS

After the needle is spun, each player of this game tries to make the point of the needle stop on his half of the board. His opponent not only tries to prevent this but also tries to prevent it from hitting a high number if he loses otherwise.

to give it a healthy spin and then try to make it stop with its point on his half of the dial or board.

You can probably think up many more games that can be played with magnets.

Chapter 6

MAGIC WITH MAGNETS

MAGNETISM is, of course, an asset to the amateur magician. It is an invisible force that can work its miracles over distances without detection by an audience. It does not need complicated mechanism. Magnets can be very easily concealed and they always work; there is nothing to get out of order.

The tricks treated in this chapter are simple and they are offered merely as samples of what may be accomplished by someone who gives a little thought to the matter. There is really no end to the things that may be done. The force of magnetism is mysterious enough when it is out in the open for all to see.

When its source is concealed, great wonderment can be easily produced and the young magician can give a performance that will leave his audience utterly at sea and singing his praises as a great master of the art of illusion.

First place a small magnet up your sleeve. One or two rubber bands can be used to hold the magnet in place as shown in the photograph. Then take a piece of some sort of magnetic material, either iron or steel. A one-inch iron washer or disk will do. Hold the washer between the thumb and the index finger and give the wrist a quick twist, flipping the washer up the sleeve.

If sufficiently powerful, the flip will send the washer far enough up the sleeve to be attracted and held by the magnet. So effective is the attraction that the performer will be able to shake his arm violently to show his audience that the washer is not concealed about his person.

The disappearing washer trick is mentioned largely to indicate the various uses that can be made of magnets for magic. A little thought will produce

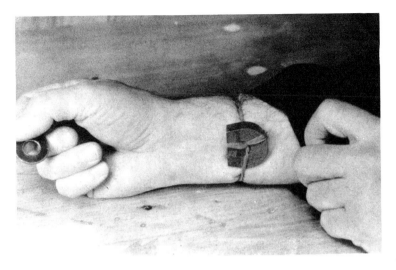

MAGNETIC PRESTO CHANGO

By concealing a strong permanent magnet up his sleeve in
this fashion, the amateur magician can flick washers out of
sight to his heart's content, without fear of detection.

many other tricks where a magnet or two, ingeni-
ously placed and properly concealed, can be used to
attract and hold objects that are to "disappear."

If you are at all clever with tools you can also make
a set of "magic blocks" that will puzzle your less in-
formed friends. As a matter of fact, you do not have
to be so clever with tools at that. Simply be cautious
and patient, because you are here faced with the

problem of carefully concealing what you do to two pieces of wood.

Two magnets will be needed for the magic blocks and you should buy two especially for this purpose because they are to be permanently encased in two pieces of soft pine. In view of the many very interesting things that you can do with the blocks, however, they will be well worth the price paid.

The blocks actually used will depend in size and shape upon the size and shape of the magnets employed. Although a horseshoe type of magnet is shown in the photograph, this does not mean that this type actually has to be used. If you have two bar magnets at hand that you would like to use, there is no reason why this cannot be done.

You will notice in the photograph that a recess has been cut into each one of the soft pine blocks. The total depth of the recesses in both of the blocks must be sufficient to cover the whole magnet. In other words, the recess in each block should be slightly deeper than half the thickness of the magnet you are using.

To cut this recess simply lay the magnet on the surface of the piece of wood and draw around it with a pencil. The outline so produced is used as a guide line in cutting the wood. The wood may be

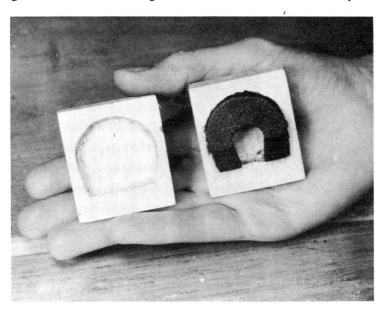

THE SECRET OF THE MAGNETIC BLOCKS

This shows how the magnet is concealed between the halves of the block. The fit should be tight to prevent the magnet from moving. If the depression is cut too big, a bit of paper can be wedged around the edges.

cut either with a small sharp chisel or a sharp jack-knife. If the outline is not strictly followed don't worry too much about it, because both of these surfaces will eventually be covered up. However, guard against producing large splinters that will carry over to the edges of either one of the pieces of wood.

After the two recesses have been cut in the halves of the block and the magnet tucked away in place, make sure that the magnet is securely in position and cannot move about or rattle. This would be a dead giveaway and must be guarded against. If the recess you have cut is a little too large, then stuff a bit of paper in between the magnet and the wood.

You now reach a point where some mechanical skill is required. You have to assemble the halves of the magic block in such a way that even the most careful examination will not reveal the line of contact. This may sound very difficult but it isn't. If you carefully follow the directions given here, you will be able to do a job of which you can be justly proud and one that will not in any way jeopardize your standing as a magician.

First make sure that the surfaces of the two sides of the block that are to come together are perfectly flat. Otherwise it will be quite impossible to join the halves in such a way as to avoid detection by a critical and snoopy member of a future audience. Of course, if you have a disk grinder in your workshop, the surfaces can be smoothed quickly and easily. If you don't, perhaps the owner of such a tool will help you out, or you can use the disk grinder in the manual training department at school. Or the surfaces can be carefully sandpapered.

When you have smoothed the two surfaces to be joined and the magnet is carefully tucked away, you are ready for the delicate matter of actual assembly. Here you must be sure of the adhesive that is to be used for this purpose. If glue is employed, it should be of the highest quality. Household cement, however, will be much better. Apply a thin layer of the adhesive over the surfaces of the two halves of the block. Remember that it must be a *thin* layer. Thick layers of adhesives do not necessarily mean better adhesion. In this case, you are going to apply such a high pressure to the two halves of the block while the adhesive is setting, that all excess will be forced out. To apply this pressure, simply mount the two halves of the block in a vise and screw it up tightly. Before this is done, however, take the precaution of placing the two halves between two pieces of wood so that the jaw marks of the vise will not be left on the surfaces of the finished article.

The block should be given twenty-four hours in which to dry or set, and then it is removed and the edges are treated to obliterate the evidence of gluing or cementing that will be left. It will be pretty hard to do this unless you can enlist the services of a power-driven disk surface sander. With the aid of such a device, no trouble will be had and a bit of treatment will remove practically every trace of the joint. Just to make sure that it will not be detected afterward, cover the magic blocks with a good grade of thick varnish, something with a bit of color to it. We said "blocks." Here it is advised that you make two such devices. You can make only one, but it will be much more fun having two. The use of two will also provide an opportunity for more interesting tricks.

The successful use of these blocks of wood before an actual audience depends to a great extent on the cleverness of the spiel by the performer. Some sly reference might be made to a "strange magnetic wood recently discovered deep in the jungles of the Malay." The performer, after such an explanation, might even risk passing the two blocks around the audience for very close examination. There will be little risk in such an invitation if the job has been done carefully. If a member of the audience suggests that the weight of the blocks is suspiciously great, he can be asked if he has ever had any experience with woods such as teak or mahogany.

We do not have the space here to give a lengthy outline of the many things that can be accomplished with these mysterious blocks. Certain it is that when their proper sides are brought together so that the pole faces of the magnets are in proper order, the blocks will attract each other. Actual adhesion can be accomplished and a certain degree of repulsion. For instance, if one block is laid flat side down on

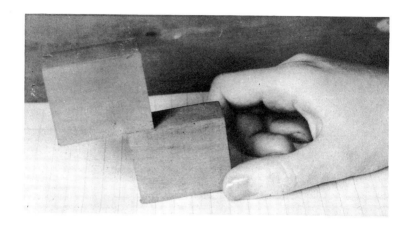

STRANGE BLOCKS FROM STRANGE WOOD

The magnetic blocks can be made to attract or repel each
other and in the hands of a clever amateur magician they can
be used with telling effect on an audience.

the table and the other block is placed over it, the
audience will notice a twisting action as the blocks
turn to bring the poles of their respective magnets
into proper relationship. Naturally, all sorts of what
might be (to the audience, at least) "gravity defying
experiments" may be made if a little thought is given
the matter.

We have not by any means exhausted the subject of magnetism as an aid to the amateur magician. But it is hoped that we have gone far enough to prove that this strange force of nature should be represented in the kit of every ambitious devotee of the black art.

Chapter 7

ELECTRICITY AND MAGNETISM

W E SAID in the earlier part of this book that electricity and magnetism were like two faces on a single coin. They are strangely interrelated and, if we study one far enough, we shall sooner or later be faced with the necessity of studying the other if we are going to make further progress. We might call them the Sister Sciences and there will come times when it will be most difficult to tell whether we are dealing with electricity or magnetism. This we do know: we would not have any electric power in the world today, as we know it and use it, were it not for this thing called magnetism. Even if we could generate such power without the aid of magnetism, as might be done with enormous sets of batteries, we could not apply this power without seeking the assistance of the force of magnetism. Later we will go into the matter of this relationship more deeply. For the moment, however, we shall merely probe the more elementary aspects of the subject.

The earliest experimenters with magnetism were not in any way conscious of the fact that this force was connected with electricity. Of course, at that time little or nothing was known about electricity. It was simply that strange terror that suddenly sprang from the clouds to rend trees, kill men and shake the earth.

Although there was much speculation concerning magnetism prior to 1600, no attempt had been made to study it in a scientific way and many of the opinions held were tainted with superstition and the scientifically unjustified concepts of black magic. It was during the year 1600 that the clever Dr. William Gilbert, an Englishman, published a book dealing with the experiments that he had made. In the light of our present knowledge of magnetism, all of his experiments were not accurately interpreted but his contributions were many and his book stood for a long time as the only meaty reference to a subject that, somehow or other, had become confused in many minds with spirits and goblins. Anyone at all fair must set Dr. Gilbert down as the Father of Magnetism.

It was not, however, until the beginning of the nineteenth century that men interested in the subject began to ponder over the curious relationship between magnetism and electricity. Galvani, an Italian physician, had discovered electric currents back in 1786 and he was quickly followed by Volta, another Italian, who constructed the first electric battery. These and other men had sensed some definite relationship between the force that made itself known with the sudden greenish-blue flash and the quiet power of attraction that seemed, up to that time at least, to be largely a resident of iron and steel. A number of silly theories were advanced by people unqualified for such work but little knowledge was contributed to lift the mysterious veil until 1819 when Hans Christian Oersted announced his marvelous discoveries that startled the scientific world of that day.

The scene was in Copenhagen and Oersted was a comparatively young, extremely clever man. The tools for investigation that he had at his disposal were simple indeed, but he had an imaginative mind and that proved to be his greatest help. Fortunately for us, some of Oersted's experiments, which at the time amounted to sensational discoveries, may be repeated with the aid of a few very simple devices. We are privileged indeed to be able to re-create such epochal experiments.

The investigations of Oersted are going to be part of the work by which we can prove to ourselves that magnetism and electricity are truly the Sister Sciences.

For our first experiment, we shall need a small compass such as is used by Boy Scouts in their meanderings. It need not be an expensive instrument; a twenty-five-cent one will do just as nicely as one costing fifty times as much. Our requirements are only that it respond with reasonable accuracy to the magnetism of the earth. Its size makes little or no difference so long as it is large enough to reveal clearly the movements of its needle. We shall also need a source of direct current such as that delivered by a dry cell. If you do not have the money needed to purchase a dry cell, then turn to a book dealing with amateur electricity. Wet cells can easily be made with materials at hand if you have any kind of a junk box at all under the workshop bench.

The materials for the first experiment are completed by the addition of a few feet of No. 18 copper wire. Enough wire for this and our later experiments can be obtained at the electrical counter of the five-and-ten for about twenty-five cents.

The setup for the first experiment is shown in the photograph on page 96. It will be noted that the wire runs over the compass and indeed should lie upon it so that the effect we seek will be easily demonstrated. Two pieces of the wire are connected to the two binding posts of the dry cell. So long as these

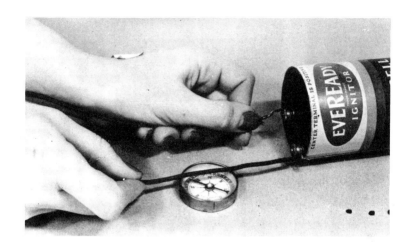

WIRES ACT LIKE MAGNETS

Any wire carrying an electric current acts like a magnet so long as the current flows. We can discover this for ourselves by placing our compass near a wire carrying current from a single dry cell.

two wires are separated from each other, no current of electricity will flow from the dry cell. It will be said that the circuit "is open."

When the bare ends of the two wires are brought together and touched, then the circuit is said to be "closed" and electricity will flow from the dry cell or battery of dry cells. When we bring these wires directly together in this fashion, the electric current flowing through them has nothing to do; no work to accomplish. Hence, something *must* happen and the electric current spends itself heating the wire through which it passes. Not only this, but the current from the dry cell will be drawn forth at such a rate as to damage the cell if the contact between the wires is held more than a few seconds. This is mentioned so that the present experiment will not wind up fatally for the dry cell. Just touching the bare ends of the two wires together occasionally will be quite sufficient to demonstrate that which we seek.

Now we are ready to proceed. With one of the wires on top of the compass case and watching the compass needle for even the slightest agitation, bring the wires together; just the barest kind of a brushing contact. Did that compass needle move? Yes, the compass needle will move under such circumstances and it will move just as positively as though we had brought our magnet near it. But, why should a compass needle move merely because a wire carrying an electric current is near it?

We can never hope to give the full answer to that simple question. And our ignorance is shared by all of the great scientists of the day. All we can say definitely about the matter is that, for some reason still not perfectly clear, an electric current passing through a wire sets up a magnetic field or magnetic lines of force about the wire. It is strange, too, that this magnetic field generated in or around a nonmagnetic material like copper or brass or indeed any kind of a conductor should be exactly the same kind of a magnetic field that we find extending outward from the poles of any kind of permanent magnet. The permanent magnet has no electric current connected with it in any way whatsoever and yet it is able to duplicate that which is produced by an ordinary wire carrying an ordinary current of electricity.

Here, for the first time, we actually rub elbows with the mysterious problem of electricity versus magnetism. If this experiment finds us baffled we are but experiencing that which has been experienced by many scientists who have gone on before us. We can ponder the question all we like; we can read the authorities, and we can speculate and experiment to our heart's content, but by and large we shall not be able to progress much further than we have already in our understanding of this strange relationship. We can certainly agree that the closest relationship exists between the two forces, but we cannot explain it. And neither, so far, have any of the great scientists who have pondered the question over the past century and a half.

There are a number of most interesting and still more baffling ramifications to this experiment. But first conduct the preceding experiment over again, taking care to note the direction in which the needle of the compass turns. Keep this in mind for future reference while you make a slight change in the arrangement of the equipment. Making sure to keep the wires in the same relative positions in relation to the compass, loosen the ends connected to the dry cell and reverse them. Check again to see that the *same piece of wire* is passing over the compass as in the first experiment. Now close the circuit by bringing the bare ends of the wires briefly into contact. As this is done keep an eye on the compass and you will note that the needle turns surely enough, but that this time it turns in the opposite direction. It is just as though you turned the compass needle first with one pole of a permanent magnet and then turned the magnet about to bring the other pole into play, a change that would cause the opposite end of the needle to respond and that would turn the needle in the other direction.

We say that our permanent magnet has a north and a south pole. This is quite true, and we can also say that our current-carrying wire, which acts as a magnet, also has a north and a south pole and that these poles can be very easily reversed by simply changing the direction of the current flowing through the wire. However, always bear in mind that this holds true only for direct current and not for the alternating current that we use in our homes.

The last experiment was one of those first performed by the master Oersted. We can still imagine how thrilled he must have been to discover such a thing. He and many others had known of the family ties between the two forces but here was the first time that actual laboratory proof had been offered. For many years it had been known that when lightning struck steel objects it left them rather heavily magnetized. In short, they became magnetized by the mere passage of the current.

What Oersted discovered, among other things, was that the needle of a compass tended to set itself at right angles to a wire carrying an electric current. As for ourselves, we can spend many hours experimenting with our compass, wire and dry cell. Many different positions for the wire in relation to the compass can be tried and in each case a slightly different effect will be obtained. Try the wire in horizontal and vertical positions and note the effect on the compass in every instance. These experiments will be fascinating and perhaps, if you aspire to be a real scientist someday, it might be well to keep notes covering the various actions of the compass under different conditions. Soon you will have a very clear and practical knowledge of the connection between electricity and magnetism as revealed with our crude in-

struments. Crude or not, they reveal basic truths in a simple and rather eloquent manner; for we are dealing here with a fundamental concept that finds wide, practical use in the everyday, workaday world of electricity.

To help your investigation into this fascinating field, assemble what was once known as a Schweigger's Multiplier. This is really a very simple instrument, easily made and easily operated; and it will add greatly to your knowledge of this subject. We might, however, offer a small objection to the term "Multiplier." The instrument is really a current detector, an electric current sleuth that will go sniffing about to ferret out weak or strong sources of electricity.

The term "Multiplier" came about in this manner. Fresh from a duplication of Oersted's famous experiments, we can easily understand that, after Oersted, someone must have reasoned this way:

If one wire carrying an electric current will set up a magnetic field, why would it not be possible to build a stronger field by winding a long piece of wire into a coil so that the magnetic field produced by the whole of the wire is bunched or concentrated into a small space?

That was good reasoning and it was correct. Johann Schweigger tried it first, and with very practical results. When he wound his wire in such a way as to leave a large opening in the center of the coil —an opening large enough to insert a compass—he devised the first useful instrument in detecting electric current. It could not measure the current except in a roughly comparative manner, but it was useful in finding current. Hence, we shall set about building such a device.

For twenty-five cents you can purchase a coil of insulated copper wire at a chain store. Such coils are usually available at the electrical counters. They are evenly wound and they may be held permanently in shape by winding a bit of heavy string or thread around them. The photograph of the detecting instrument shows how neat they are.

Our little current-detecting device is simple enough. It amounts to nothing more or less than a baseboard holding the coil and a small shelf arranged

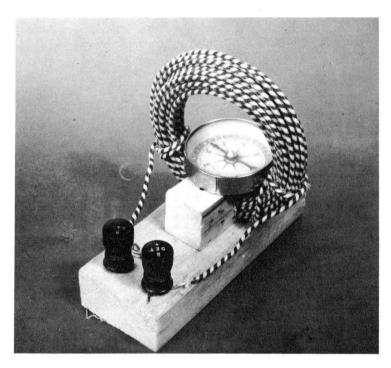

A MARVELOUS CURRENT DETECTOR

A compass placed in the middle of a small coil of wire becomes a fine detector for electric current. When a current passes through the coil of wire, it sets up a magnetic field which is able to move the compass needle.

in the center of the coil, the compass sitting on the shelf. The two ends of the wire coming from the coil are stripped of insulation for the distance of an inch or so and these bare ends are then fastened under two machine screws or binding posts. A professional touch will be added to the instrument if you give it a single coat of orange shellac after it is finished and before the compass is mounted in place. Shellac is used a great deal by electricians because it resists moisture and also because it makes an excellent insulator.*

If you stop to analyze the little electric current detector, you will see that you have an instrument capable of amplifying or increasing the magnetic field generated by an electric current. That is really all there is to it.

After you set the compass in the center of the coil, you are ready for the first test. One wire from the dry cell (either one) is connected to one of the binding posts of the instrument and the other binding post is touched with the other wire to complete the circuit.

*An insulator is a substance or material that prevents the passage of electric current. If it were not for insulators of various kinds, we would not be able to confine electricity to wires or instruments at all. It would go running through everything and we would never be able to make any use of it.

As you do this, watch the compass needle. The needle is violently disturbed for an instant but rapidly comes to rest in a new position. This position will depend entirely upon the direction of the electric current flowing through the coil. If you wish to shift the wires on the dry cell, as we did once before, you will note that the needle of the compass will do precisely the same thing but in a different direction. A full-fledged electrician would say that you had changed the "polarity" of the current by shifting from the positive to the negative and vice versa.

Just as a magnet has a north and south pole, so does a dry cell (or a dynamo, for that matter) have a positive and a negative pole. There can be no doubt about it: these poles are very definitely related. Any coil of wire carrying a direct current of electricity, such as that delivered by a dry cell or a battery of cells, has a north and a south pole, the location of each depending entirely upon the direction in which the electric current is passing through the coil. No one really knows in which direction electricity flows. For many years electrons were thought to move from the positive (plus +) pole to the negative (minus −) pole. Now many experts are of the opinion that the reverse is true; that is, that the flow is from negative to positive. There is no reason for the young reader to become involved in this controversy, but he should bear in mind that the direction of flow of electricity *is* a controversial question and that neither theory has ever been proved. In any event, the important thing is that we know that electrons do move; for the purposes of the young experimenter, the direction of their flow is not important.

Many experiments can be made using the current detector as a polarity indicator. For this reason, mark the terminals or binding posts of the device in such a way as to assist you in the future when you wish to make use of it in this way.

The instrument is connected to a dry cell and the direction of movement taken by the needle is carefully noted. Check also the connections to the dry cell. In case the terminals on the dry cell are not marked positive and negative, it can be taken for granted that the center binding post is positive and the outside post is negative. The binding post on the current detector that is connected to the positive or center post of the dry cell is so marked. Here, with a pencil, place a large plus (+) sign. It follows, of course, that if this post is positive, then the opposite post must be negative, and it is so marked (−). The direction taken by the needle is also noted and a pencil notation is placed on the instrument. For instance, say "Needle to the right, Positive." Then, later, you will know that when the needle turns in the opposite direction the positive pole marked on the current detector will no longer be positive but negative.

We should never under any circumstances connect this current dectector permanently to any source of electric current. Simply connect either one or the other of the wires to one of the binding posts on the device and touch the second terminal or binding post with the bare end of the second wire. If this instrument were left connected to a dry cell or a battery of dry cells for more than a few seconds, the cell or battery would be ruined. It is not within the province of this book to go into this matter, but we can put it down as something that should never be done.

We have been dabbling with electricity and magnetism in an effort to demonstrate the relationship between the two. Hence, it is logical here to bring the two words together to form the term electromagnetism, a compound word which has been in use for many years. The coil in your current detector is technically referred to as an electromagnet, which may be defined as a device used to generate a magnetic field. Electromagnetism is magnetism generated by electric current, as distinguished from magnetism produced by permanent magnets.

There is a distinct limitation to what we can do with our present current detector. However, with just one more device, we can set out on a series of experiments that may take days to complete. The additional equipment recommended amounts to another coil, the same as the first one. This means the expenditure of only another twenty-five cents. Or a trip to the local electrical shop, with a statement of the purpose we have in mind, might bring response in the nature of some used wire. You need only twenty or thirty feet of it and the size may range anywhere between 18 and 26 gauge. The wire must be insulated, of course, since you are to make a coil of it.

To make the coil, simply wind the wire around something of the right diameter — say about 3 inches. After the wire or coil is removed from the winding form, wind thread or string around it to preserve its shape. You will then be prepared to set off on some really exciting experiments.

The first one is going to be a duplication of a very famous experiment that not only demonstrates the kinship of magnetism and electricity, but also shows that there are other ways of generating current electricity; that is, other than by chemical cells.

You will not need your dry cell for this experiment. The setup is simple, too, as a glance at the photograph will show. Simply connect the two coils directly together, making sure that the second coil is removed from the current detector by a foot or so.

After the apparatus has been set up, take a bar magnet and plunge it quickly into the center of the free, or second, coil — at the same time looking at the needle of the compass resting in the center of our current detector. If the compass is sensitive enough (and

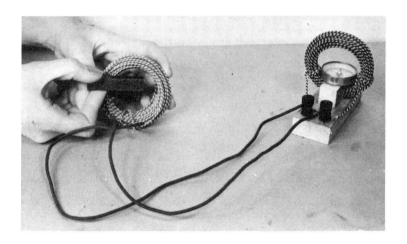

DEMONSTRATING THE PRINCIPLE
OF THE DYNAMO

A second coil is connected to the coil on the current detector. When a magnet is moved near the second coil a current will be generated in it and detected by the compass needle. This is really the principle of the electric dynamo.

it should be, unless it is a defective one), the needle will give a sudden jerk at the instant you plunge the magnet into the center of the coil.

But why should this happen? Was the needle of the compass moved merely by the magnet? To check on this point, take the magnet to another position about two or three feet from the coil and move it, at the same time watching the needle of the compass. The needle either does not move or, if it is an extremely sensitive instrument and does move slightly, it does not move nearly so much as it did when you plunged the magnet into the center of the coil. Something has gone surging along the wire connecting the two coils together. The force, whatever it is, has been transmitted over a distance and has been carried by the copper conductors. What is it?

We should be able to guess accurately. Current alone will not in any way affect a compass needle. Only magnetism will produce the shudder you noticed. Somehow or other that magnetism must have been generated by the coil surrounding the compass. How did it get there?

You can now appreciate how confusing those early experiments must have been to the first experimenters. Just imagine, at this point, being left to your own mental devices and being faced with the necessity of actually determining what has transpired in this simple little experiment. The "simple little experiment" would pose momentous questions indeed. You would be groping about in darkness. You could not go to the library for a book that would tell all about what you had been doing. We are at a point where great things that once happened are about to be duplicated and a moment of appreciation for the work of the great minds of the past is in no sense out of place.

As we ponder the problem before us, we are at a loss to analyze it. Speculation on the point is very apt to produce rather barren results because, after all, we are confronted with a problem that once bothered some really great minds. Therefore, we had better stop guessing and humble ourselves to the point of taking a little instruction.

When a magnet is moved in the vicinity of a coil

of wire, the coil of wire is said to "cut through" the invisible magnetic lines of force and, for reasons still not clear, an electric current is generated in a coil under these circumstances. We had better accept this bald statement just as it is. But we repeat; an electric current will be generated in a wire when a magnet is moved near it. Upon this simple but mysterious thing rests the whole world of electricity as it affects our daily lives. If an electric current were NOT generated under such conditions, the world would never have had the luxuries provided by electricity.

Of course, the mere fact that an electric current will be generated in a coil that is near a moving magnet (or a moving coil that is near a still magnet for that matter) does not explain all the details of the experiment that we have just conducted.

However, if a current is generated in a coil by plunging a magnet into it, we know that this current must have flowed through the connecting wires and also into the coil of the current detector. We have already learned that a current flowing through a wire or coil will generate a magnetic field. Thus the detector coil generated its own field and this, in turn, reached out and gave the compass needle a little jerk.

We are now ready to formulate some pretty important laws, although we must not lose sight of the fact that the one just laid down is the *most* important one that we shall be called upon to recognize. It is basic and fundamental and all the others about to be brought to the fore spring from it.

Let us again try the experiment of plunging the magnet into the free coil. This time watch the needle of the compass very carefully so that you can check its movements as closely as possible. Perhaps the needle did little more than jerk the first time, and as true scientists it behooves us to try each experiment over and over again, watching for *little things* that may offer big clues.

If we are careful, we shall note that the needle points in one direction when the magnet is plunged in, and in the opposite direction when it is withdrawn. That is something else over which we can ponder. Of course, we have a clue here. Did we not learn that the needle of a compass would move in one way for a current going in one direction and in another way for a current going in the opposite direction? According to our present investigation, then, we must have had two different currents, one going in one direction and the other going in the opposite direction.

If you have a good analytical mind, you will recall that we moved the magnet in two different directions — in and out. A check will show that the current reversed itself when the direction of the movement of the magnet was reversed. Better put that fact down in your notebook for it is an important one to remember. What we really did, if you think about it, was to generate an alternating current that displayed just two cycles or reversals. If we plunged the magnet into the coil and pulled it out repeatedly at high speed, we would generate an alternating current. In truth, we have what has become known as an alternator or an alternating current generator.

A little thinking along with these experiments and a little close observation will reveal many things that might otherwise pass unnoticed. The careful young experimenter will certainly notice that there is some relationship between the amount of current generated and the speed with which the magnet moves. If the magnet is quickly plunged into the center of the coil, a greater current will be generated. Here, however, we must not be unmindful of the fact that we can move the magnet faster than our compass needle will respond so that we must not regard failure here as a flaw in our theory. We also find that we can move the magnet so slowly through the center of what might be called the "pick-up coil" that the compass will not respond at all, the current generated being too weak.

There are two things that cause a larger volume of current to pass through the circuit: a larger magnet and the faster movement of the magnet. We can formulate another electromagnetic law on this point. We can say, with scientific truth, that the current generated by the coil and the magnet will depend upon how many magnetic lines of force pass through the coil and the speed with which they pass.

If we had a larger magnet, then we would generate a great deal more current in the coil when the magnet was waved or moved near by.

In the past, we have been talking about moving the magnet through the center of the coil. This is not necessary but it is perhaps the best way of generating the largest possible current. If we simply move the magnet past the coil a current will be generated in it. The farther away the magnet is when it passes, the weaker the resultant current. It is all very simple but, at the same time, very wonderful.

What would happen if we just left the magnet motionless near the coil? This should not take very long to find out. The experiment can be made in a minute or two. Bring the magnet near the coil, hold it motionless and watch for results at the current detector. There is no movement of the needle because no current will be generated so long as the magnet is not moved. This is just exactly as it should be. We could not, as scientists, expect anything but such a result. If we did, we would not believe in that great scientific code called the Law of the Conservation of Energy. This is a pretty high-sounding title, perhaps.

It might be more understandable if we called it, instead, the You-Can't-Have-Something-For-Nothing Law. In short, says the Law of the Conservation of Energy: "If you want to generate power or electricity, you must exert force." If this law were not true, a perpetual-motion machine would have been invented hundreds of years ago—all we would have to do would be to set large magnets in the center of large coils and electricity would be generated without further fuss or bother.

Another question will surely occur to us. Does it make any difference which is moved, the coil or the magnet? We can easily prove that it does not. Set the magnet up on a box and wave the small coil near it. The compass needle will respond as it responded when the reverse experiment was conducted.

The subject of electromagnetism is doubtlessly one of the most fascinating subjects in the whole sweep of science. It is like a great mystery story unraveling itself before our very eyes. We can make many experiments until, at last, we can learn no more about it save how it acts under certain circumstances and how to control it. We cannot ever hope to learn anything about its fundamental nature.

There is one curious thing that must stand out, though, if you give the matter much thought. Whether you realize it or not, we have discovered, quite by ourselves, that under certain conditions electric currents can be made to create magnetic fields and that, conversely, magnetic fields can generate electric currents. That is something to think about!

Chapter 8

WE BUILD A BIG ELECTROMAGNET

W E have now become acquainted with all the basic laws of magnetism and electromagnetism. You have covered a great deal of ground and should now be prepared for new adventures.

There are many different materials in the world, some 500,000 of them. A few of them conduct electric current very well, but most of them conduct it either not at all or very grudgingly. All the metals, for instance, are comparatively good conductors of electricity, but glass is a very poor one. For this reason, we say that materials such as glass, sulphur and porcelain are insulators or bad conductors. Electricity *can* be forced through them under certain circumstances, but it is difficult to accomplish.

Although there is some relationship, conductors and nonconductors of magnetism should not be confused with those of electricity. As electricity, magnetism also has its favorites, its likes and dislikes. This strange force passes through some materials with ease, but in other cases, most of it is almost stopped dead in its tracks. For instance, magnetism will pass through materials such as glass and paper very easily. Iron, however, will stop it and capture it, so to speak.

When a piece of soft iron is exposed to a magnetic field, it seems that the magnetic lines of force almost go out of their way to bend toward the iron and to pass through it, thus making the iron itself magnetic. For this reason, soft iron is of great use in the workaday world of electricity, and the next experiment will illustrate this point.

We are going to make what the electricians call an electromagnet; that is, a magnet in which the magnetism is produced by the passage of electric current. We'll need a soft iron bolt about ½ inch in diameter and about 4 inches long. This is known as a carriage bolt, and you can obtain one at the local hardware store for about three cents.

Inasmuch as you must wind this bolt with wire, you will have to choose between using the wire from one of your coils or buying some additional wire. If you can afford the expenditure of another twenty-five cents, you should buy a new coil of bell wire and preserve your equipment. After all, you may wish to go back to it.

The work involved in the construction of an electromagnet does not amount to much. Simply wind the whole coil of wire on the core, the core in this case being the soft iron bolt. After the wire is wound in place, secure it in some way. Several kinks may be used, or if there is some binding tape about the house, ask for a yard or so. This is wound over the wire, the end is glued or cemented in place and the whole thing is given a coat of shellac. When the shellac dries, the tape will be held permanently in position. You are now ready to experiment with this new addition to your equipment.

Perhaps you have already guessed that the soft iron core of the electromagnet will become highly magnetized if you pass an electric current through the coil. That is right. Due to the ease with which the soft iron in the center of the coil will conduct magnetism, a great many of the magnetic lines of force generated by the current passing through the coil will be concentrated in the center. This makes the ends of the bolt magnetic, as you will see when the wires of the coil are connected to your dry cell. Here, however, you must again be warned not to leave the connection for more than a few seconds at a time else you exhaust the dry cell. Electricians would say that the little coil has a "low resistance" and would draw too much current to be healthy for a tiny dry cell. Of course, there is really no need for leaving this connection in place too long because most experiments can be conducted in a very short time.

The imaginative worker will want to try many

experiments with this new piece of equipment. For one thing, he will want to know what relationship this new kind of magnet might have to the permanent magnets used in our earlier experiments. Does this magnet, for instance, have a north and a south pole? Does it have the property of repulsion like other magnets? There is only one good way to answer these questions and that is experimentally; let us find the answers ourselves.

For the first experiment, you will need one of your permanent magnets. After connecting the electromagnet to the dry cell, bring one pole of the permanent magnet near one end of the electromagnet. One of two things will happen, depending upon the kind of poles that meet. You will find that the electromagnet has poles too, their location depending upon the direction in which the current is passing through the coil. If you obtain attraction when you place the pole of the permanent magnet near the pole of the electromagnet, then you know that two opposite poles have been brought together.

The foregoing experiment proves that an electromagnet excited with direct current will behave just like a permanent magnet in many respects. Its strength —that is, its power to move and lift iron and steel objects—will depend upon how much wire there is in the coil and the amount of electric current passing through this coil. There are a few other factors in the case, but these are the major ones. If you added another dry cell to the one you have, making a battery of two, the power of the electromagnet would be greatly increased. The current from three dry cells would produce more magnetism still, and you can put it down as a rule for these electromagnets that the amount of magnetism produced by them will depend upon the current passing through them.

What happens to the magnetism in the soft iron core of the electromagnet after the current has been turned off? That sounds like a pretty sensible question. Offhand we might say that it would completely disappear, but this is not so. The bolt will hold some of this magnetism and will, in a sense, become a very weak permanent magnet after its first baptism of current. Ordinarily, this "residual magnetism," as the electricians call it, would escape our attention. Just to prove that what has been said is true, we shall make a quick experimental check. A tiny sliver of sheet iron or steel is cut from a larger piece and this is brought in contact with the end of the iron bolt after the current has been cut off. The bolt will hold the small piece of metal and it will be quite difficult to shake it off.

There is one simple way in which the bolt could be deprived of its residual magnetism. If we heated it to redness in a fire and allowed it to cool slowly, its magnetic property would completely disappear. There is still another way to demagnetize materials, but it is a bit too technical to come within the scope of this book.

If you have a model railroad, some very interesting experiments can be performed with the transformer that comes with it. It will be recalled that this device reduces the voltage of the alternating house current to a point where it is safe to use. It would be most interesting, indeed, to connect such

ELECTRICITY GENERATES MAGNETISM

When wire is wound around a soft iron bolt and current is sent through the wire, a powerful magnetic field will be created and the bolt will become magnetized.

a source of current to your electromagnet. We have in the past been using direct current and it may be that curious things will happen with alternating current.

Before the first experiment is conducted, we must

issue another warning. Under no circumstances should the electromagnet be left connected to the transformer for more than a minute or so at a time. You need have no fear here that your current supply will give out, as in the case of the dry cell. Just the reverse is true, for you have here a supply that will not stop until some damage has been done. If the small coil is left connected to the transformer for too long a period, both the coil and the transformer will heat up to a dangerous point. And in no case should you use the highest voltage of the transformer. It is best that the regulator be set at the first point.

Observing the above precautions, connect the electromagnet to the transformer. Now take a screw driver or some similar tool of steel or iron and hold it to one end of the iron bolt. Pull gently. When this is done, the screw driver is set to vibrating. It will beat a high-pitched staccato on the end of the bolt. What has happened? Let's think about this for a moment.

Sometime back we stated that alternating current is a to-and-fro affair: it goes first in one direction and then the other, reversing its direction many times a second. When it reverses itself 120 times a second, it is called 60-cycle alternating current and this is the kind of current used in most homes. It follows that when the alternating current in the coil reverses itself, the poles of the coil follow it. For a brief part of a second, one pole will be north, and the next instant it will be south. In the case of a 60-cycle current, one end of the bolt will be north sixty times a second and south sixty times a second.

The cause of the vibration should now be clear. Sixty times a second the screw driver will be attracted by the electromagnet. Sixty times a second it will be repelled by it. Thus we see that alternating current does not produce the steady pull or repulsion that is produced by direct current.

We are going to try another experiment with the transformer, and for this one you will need your current detector. One wire from the current detector is connected to one of the terminals of the transformer. The other wire from the current detector is brought near the other terminal of the transformer but is not fixed to it. This wire is simply touched to the terminal of the transformer and then quickly removed. If we watch the needle of the compass when the wire is touched to the terminal of the transformer, we will note that the needle gives a jerk and spins around. After that, it remains perfectly still. If you

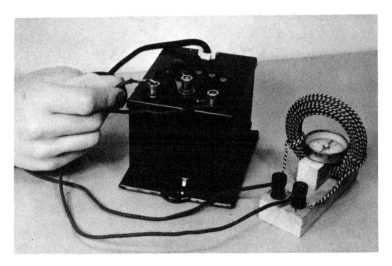

AN ELECTRICAL WHIRLIGIG

When connected to a toy transformer in this fashion, the needle of the current detector can be made to spin at high speed if the current is permitted to flow but momentarily by barely touching the connector.

connect and disconnect the current quickly enough, the compass needle will spin around at high speed.

Is there something wrong here? Has one of our theories gone bad on us? It will be recalled that the compass needle acted in about the same way in response to direct current. The needle of the current detector would give a little jerk when the current was turned on and it would then remain motionless. But in this case the current is turning itself on and off 120 times a second. Should it not follow that the needle should respond to this action? Indeed, it does follow, but for mechanical reasons the needle just can't change its direction of motion that fast. This is due to the force of inertia, or what we might call the laziness of matter. The needle does not respond to the changes in the alternating current because these changes take place too quickly to overcome the inertia of the needle and make it move. This experiment is important because it shows that another force is at work here which our eyes cannot see. That is something the scientist must always be on the lookout for.

We are now going to build another electromagnet,

a different kind. This time, in place of winding the wire around a bolt, wind it around a tube. The tube can be made of anything except iron or steel and it should not be over ½ inch in diameter. If the worst comes to the worst, we can build up such a tube with layers of paper, winding the paper around a wooden form and using plenty of shellac so that the paper tube will be sturdy enough for our purposes. A fiber tube ½ inch in diameter and 4 or 5 inches long would be just the thing if you can get it. Aluminum, brass or copper would also do. If you cannot find a piece of tubing of the right size and of the right kind of material, use a small piece of sheet brass or copper and "roll your own." This should be easy. Simply cut a piece of sheet metal the right size and bend it into the shape of a tube. If you can handle a soldering iron, it would be advisable to run it along the seam.

The tube is then wound with a twenty-five-cent coil of the insulated bell wire mentioned previously. With this in place, you have an electromagnet with a hollow center. Such things are called solenoids and they are of great use in the world of electricity. To demonstrate this use, take a ¼-inch carriage bolt and cut off the head. A bolt about 5 inches long would be just the right size. It should also fit loosely in the tube in the center of the coil.

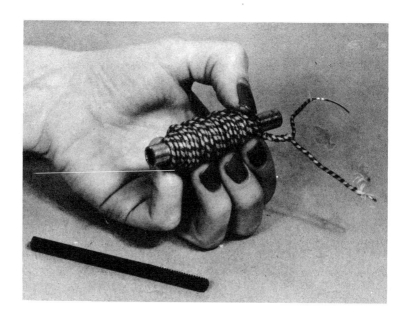

THE MAGNET WITH THE HOLLOW CENTER

Electromagnets with hollow centers are called solenoids by the electricians. They are made by winding wire around a tube.

A SOLENOID WITH ITS MOVEABLE CORE

Wire is wound around a brass or copper tube with an internal diameter large enough to accommodate a soft iron bolt. When current passes through the wire, the bolt will be pulled to the center of the tube.

For the first experiment, place the end of the bolt in the tube and then connect the coil or solenoid to the dry cell for a moment. Immediately the current passes through the coil, the carriage bolt will be violently drawn to the center of the tube. If you try the same thing at the other end of the tube, you will get the same results. The piece of soft iron will always wind up resting in the center of the tube. This is because the magnetic field produced by the coil pulls with equal force at both ends of the tube and the bolt must therefore take a position midway.

If you can get hold of an old pair of radiotelephone

HOW ELECTRICITY JUMPS ACROSS SPACE

These coils are not connected electrically, yet part of the current flowing through the coil connected to the toy transformer will pass into the second coil connected to the telephone receiver, where a loud hum will be heard.

receivers, you can conduct an experiment with two coils that will reveal the principle of the common transformer. The arrangement of the apparatus needed is shown in the photograph. Here there are two coils, a toy transformer and a pair of telephone receivers.

Note that one coil is connected to the transformer and the other is connected to the telephone receivers. When current passes through the coil connected to the transformer, the result will be heard in the receiver as a loud hum. The hum will continue as long as the current from the transformer flows through the coil.

Direct current would not act in this manner. If, in place of the transformer, you connected a dry cell to the coil and placed the telephone receivers over your head, you would hear only a single click at the moment the coil was connected to the cell. As a matter of fact, current in the second coil would flow only at this instant, even though it kept on flowing in the coil connected to the dry cell.

This is a bit difficult to understand. Perhaps a little explanation will help to make clear why alternating current will keep current flowing in the second coil while direct current will not.

Sometime back we talked about the necessity of keeping a magnet moving in the center of a coil if electric current is to be generated in that coil. We found by actual experiment that as soon as the permanent magnet stopped moving, the current stopped also. The same holds true for magnetic fields called upon to produce currents in a nearby coil through a process called electromagnetic induction. If direct current were used in the preceding experiment, the magnetic field would simply move outward from the coil as the current was turned on, cut through the second coil connected to the telephone receivers and then stand still. It would still be there, but it would be perfectly motionless.

This is not true in the case of alternating current. The alternating current goes back and forth in an electric circuit and the magnetic field set up by it follows along. It is constantly building up and collapsing; constantly reaching out only to fall again as the current goes to zero and reverses its direction. In short, the magnetic field produced by an alternating current flowing through a coil is constantly moving, constantly active, and for this reason a counterpart of such a current will be produced in a nearby coil. The hum we hear in the telephone receivers is proof of this.

Of course, this is exactly the way in which transformers operate. Some people think that transformers are used to change alternating current to direct current. Such is not the case. A device intended for this would be called a converter or a rectifier, not a transformer. Transformers are used only in connection with alternating current and they are used for two purposes only: either to increase or decrease the voltage and current of such electricity. All such transformers have two coils: the coil into which the current enters and the coil by which the current leaves. The first coil is called the primary and the second coil the secondary of the transformer. In the preceding experiment, we really had two transformers connected together. The coil connected to the toy transformer functioned as the primary, and the coil connected to the receivers as the secondary. The toy device was much more efficient than our own, however, and for a very good reason. The coils of all such transformers are always wound on soft iron cores or centers. We have already learned that iron conducts magnetism very efficiently. Air is not

PROVING THAT IRON IS A
BETTER CONDUCTOR THAN AIR

When this experiment was conducted earlier, we did not have the iron rod between the coils. When this is inserted as shown, the hum in the telephone receivers will be much louder, proving that iron conducts magnetism better than air.

such a good conductor. We can prove this point easily if we have a good heavy piece of soft iron bar.

The experiment is shown in the photograph. Instead of depending upon air to conduct the magnetism between the two coils, we insert the piece of soft iron. We note that the hum in the telephone receivers is now much louder, proving that a higher current flows in the second coil due to the presence of the soft iron.

So much for electromagnetism. In the next chapter we shall learn something about the uses that are made of this force.

Chapter 9

THE NEW MIRACLES OF MAGNETISM

N OW THAT we have come to learn something more about the strange force of magnetism, we will briefly explore its application in today's world. Almost everywhere we turn in America today, we will find magnetism at work. It is helping to operate TV stations, railroads, factories, mines, atom smashers, airplanes and even hospitals.

Next to electricity itself, magnetism is one of the world's most useful forces. Many of the wonders that we have today would be impossible without it. Magnetism, along with electricity and gravity, is one of

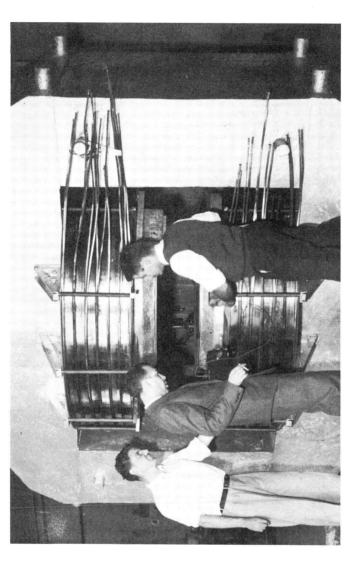

A GIANT ELECTROMAGNET IN THE MAKING

This electromagnet, weighing many tons, is an essential part of an atom smasher being assembled in the Physics Laboratory of the University of Illinois.

the three forces that is closely tied up with the mystery of the universe and even life itself.

Were it not for magnetism, there would be no electric motors, no telegraphs, no telephones, no radios, no television, no generators or dynamos, no electric phonographs, no motion pictures, no electronic brains, no guided missiles or many of the other things in the marvelous world in which we live. All these would be impossible were it not for the thin, invisible fingers of magnetism that reach out through space, that attract and repel, that vibrate at high speed or create electric currents that go surging through millions upon millions of electric motors throughout the world.

Perhaps most important of all, there would be no commercial electricity as we know it today, in home and in factory, were it not for magnetism. Without magnetism, which makes dynamos and generators possible, we would have only static electricity, which cannot supply electric power in large volume.

While it is true that sizeable amounts of electricity can be generated by thermoelectric batteries (literally heat batteries), such batteries are today a long way from supplying the power needed for the world. These batteries would not need magnetism for their operation. However, electromagnetism would still be necessary for the commercial and home use of electric power, no matter how generated.

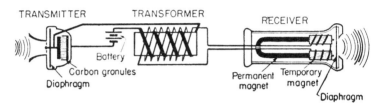

TRANSMITTER   TRANSFORMER   RECEIVER

Battery
Carbon granules
Diaphragm
Permanent magnet   Temporary magnet
Diaphragm

THE ESSENTIALS OF A TELEPHONE CIRCUIT

Sound waves entering the mouthpiece of the transmitter or microphone vibrate its diaphragm, which in turn packs and loosens the carbon granules therein. This varies the amount of current passing through the microphone and thereby impresses the sound upon the electric current, causing it to vary in accordance with the sound. The small metal diaphragm in the receiver vibrates accordingly and thereby reproduces the sound sent by the transmitter. Both the transformer and the telephone receiver shown are electromagnetic devices. (*Courtesy General Electric Co.*)

The modern American home as we know it today would be impossible without magnetism. Were

THE ELECTRON MICROSCOPE

The amazing electron microscope, which makes it possible to magnify 100,000 times. It is used both in medical and industrial research. The lenses in this microscope are made up of electromagnetic coils instead of optical glass. (*Courtesy Radio Corporation of America*) it not for magnetism, there might not be any electric lights, automatic oil or gas heat, stereophonic or hi-fi phonographs, electric razors, electric refrigerators, electric heaters, electric stoves or electric vacuum cleaners. Magnetism is so closely tied up with modern American life that were its force suddenly to cease, America would be in a panic of despair.

One of the greatest wonders made possible by magnetism is the electron microscope. This is a microscope that utilizes electrons in place of ordinary light. The degree of magnification possible with the ordinary microscope is relatively small. It usually does not exceed 2500 diameters of 2500X. This means that a small object such as a germ or virus can be magnified 2500 times. This is called the power of the microscope.

Such power as noted above is far below that made possible with the electron microscope. Such microscopes utilize beams of high-speed electrons for magnifying things. These electron beams cannot be focused with glass lenses. However, they can be brought to focus by means of magnetic coils. Hence, the lenses of an electron microscope are magnetic.

Electron microscopes are able to magnify 100,-000 times (diameters) instead of the 2500 times of the ordinary optical or glass lens microscopes. These newer microscopes have become important tools in medical and industrial research.

Were it not for magnetism all forms of sound recording and telephoning would be impossible. Even telephoning by wire or by radio would be impossible, as would radio broadcasting.

Electronic recording of sound on phonograph records was introduced some thirty-five years ago. An electromagnetic device was employed to engrave or cut the vibrations of sound into master records used to make duplicate records by a pressing process.

Another electromagnetic device called a pick-up was then employed to convert the recorded sound back into sound that could be heard. This reproduced sound was heard through the use of another electro-magnetic device called a loudspeaker.

Although present hi-fi stereophonic-recording and reproducing devices are vast improvements over the old phonograph, the principles on which they operate are pretty much the same. Again, without electromagnetism, today's hi-fi reproducing and recording systems would be impossible.

The perfection of magnetic recording on iron or steel tape and wire followed the perfection of electromagnetic recording and reproduction on wax or plastic records. This new form of magnetic recording is close to final perfection.

Some of the experiments explained in this book showed us that a magnet can be used to generate an electric current if the magnet is moved near a coil of wire. When current passes through a telephone receiver or microphone, this current can be made to carry sound. The microphone modulates the current when sound enters the microphone. By modulating, we mean that the current is varied by having the sound impressed upon it. Then, in place of the current flowing smoothly and uniformly through the microphone, it flows along in an uneven fashion. When a high sound strikes the microphone, the electric current increases. When a low sound strikes the microphone, the electric current decreases. Thus the sound impresses itself on the electric current passing through the microphone circuit. Electron tube amplifiers increase this effect.

This amplified sound current is then passed through coils with iron cores. As steel wire or tape is passed between these coils carrying the sound current, the wire or tape will be magnetized in accordance with the sound current. Thus a magnetic record of the sound will be left on the tape or wire.

To reproduce this magnetically recorded sound, we need only to pass the tape or wire between similar coils. Then the varying degrees of magnetism recorded on the tape or wire according to the sound pattern will cause varying degrees of electric current to be set up in the coils. This current will follow the same pattern as that passed through the microphone during the recording of the sound. The sound current in the reproducing coils is once more amplified with vacuum tubes and carried to loudspeakers.

Magnetic tapes are also used with some types of the electronic-brain machines, sometimes called

AN ELECTRONIC-MAGNETIC BRAIN

One of the most exciting new miracles of magnetism and electronics. This is an electronic-magnetic brain developed for the automatic translation of Russian into English. The machine is called a Decoder. Mr. E. J. Quinby, shown with one of the parts of the brain, helped in its design and construction. (*Courtesy Shepard Laboratories, Summit, New Jersey*) computers. These machines not only work out complicated mathematical problems but they also "memorize" certain data. Memorizing is done electromagnetically.

Even radar is not without its debt to magnetism. What is known as the deflection coil has made the radarscope possible.

Most of us have had the experience of passing through doors controlled by so-called electric eyes (photoelectric cells). While the photoelectric cell itself does not depend upon magnetism, the electric relay—the key device in automatic door openers—is an electromagnetic device. Indeed, wherever and however a photoelectric cell is in use in industry, shop or home, the magnetic relay is usually associated with it.

Magnetism is hard at work also in our hospitals. The very high voltages used for operating X-ray machines are generated by transformers that operate on electromagnetic principles.

The wonderful machine used to record heartbeats in hospitals depends upon electromagnetism for its

TELEVISION TAPE RECORDER

Television pictures and sound are recorded on this magnetic
tape and then transmitted over television stations for home
viewing. Someday a new form of photography may be
developed from this idea. (*Courtesy Radio Corporation of
America*)

operation. These machines are called electrocardio-graphs, and are used to detect heart trouble.

We are surrounded by scientific miracles which are dependent to some extent upon the effects of electromagnetism. In addition to those already mentioned, we might add, among countless others: automatic railway signals, diesel-electric locomotives, ignition for automobiles, and even the nuclear-powered submarine. By now we must realize how important a part this wonderful force plays in our lives.

One of the most exciting new inventions which utilizes electromagnetism is the magnetic video recorder. Video is that part of television waves that carry the picture. The audio carries the sound. Both of these signals, the video and the audio, can be recorded on magnetic tape. A new device which can be attached to home TV receivers makes such recordings automatically. If a family is to be absent from home during one of its favorite programs, the program can be recorded and played (sound) and viewed (video) back when the family returns home.

If the program is to be on at, say, 8:00 P.M., a clock

arrangement is pre-set. Then, at 8:00 P.M., the automatic magnetic recorder is thrown into action and both the picture and the sound are magnetically recorded.

The most common type of atom-smashing machine in use today is largely dependent upon the force of magnetism. We refer to the smasher known as the cyclotron. The larger types of these machines have great electromagnets that weigh many tons. With such machines, often called atomic whirligigs, atomic particles can be speeded up faster and still faster until they reach a speed of many thousands of miles, not per hour, but per second. As the atomic particles swing around and around at superspeeds, they spiral outward. Finally they reach an exit passage at the outer edge of the great machine. Then they go crashing into what is known as the target chamber. Here the particles smash into one of the many chemical elements bringing basic changes in the structure of the atoms of such elements.

As these words are being written, magnetism is being used in what could become, when it is per-

THE HEAR-AND-SEE MAGNETIC TAPE RECORDER

The recorder is shown at the left of the picture. This new machine automatically records television programs (both sound and pictures) while the family is away. When the family returns, the tape recording can be played back through the ordinary home receiver. (*Courtesy Radio Corporation of America*) fected, one of the world's most important inventions. This is a machine in which atomic energy is released by the use of a completely new process.

In the ordinary atomic bomb or nuclear-power generator, power is generated by breaking up the atoms of matter. This process is known as fission. A second method of releasing atomic energy is called fusion. Fusion is the exact opposite of fission. It is a method of bringing atoms together in such a way that part of their energy is released. The potential importance of the perfection of this process is staggering to contemplate. For instance, it is known that a cubic mile of sea water contains enough fusion material to keep our country running for 15,000 years at its present rate of power consumption.

It is the process of atomic fusion that keeps our sun hot and radiant, a process that has been going on for millions, even billions, of years. Now, for the first time, we have been able to reproduce this process on earth, though so far we know how to do it only with certain kinds of atoms. We first achieved atomic fusion with the terrible hydrogen or thermonuclear

A MODEL OF THE C STELLARATOR

This is a fusion machine that duplicates the nuclear action going on in the sun. The nuclear action takes place within the tube shown. The highly heated fusion matter is prevented from touching the walls of the tube by means of the electromagnetic coils wound around the outside of the tube. These produce what has become known as the "magnetic pinch effect." (*Courtesy Radio Corporation of America*) bomb. More recently a new method has been devised over which we have better control and in which there is no explosion.

What has become known as the fourth state of matter is used in the new method. This state of matter is neither solid, liquid nor gaseous. The new form of matter is called plasma (not to be confused with blood plasma).

Matter in a plasmic state is made up of atomic particles, and when they are in motion, these particles behave just like an electric current. Earlier in this book, we learned how electric current running through wires can be influenced by magnets. We also learned something about the close relationship between electricity and magnetism. We discovered that magnetism could be used to generate electric current and that electricity generated magnetism. Therefore, when it is said that matter in a plasmic state is made up of charged atomic particles and behaves like an electric current, we must realize that matter in this state can be controlled by magnetism.

The temperature reached by plasmic matter goes

into the millions of degrees. There is no substance on earth that could withstand direct contact with such highly heated matter. Hence, it is necessary to keep such matter out of contact with the container that holds it. This is done with electromagnetic coils. These coils are so arranged about the container that what has become known as the "magnetic pinch effect" is produced, and the plasmic matter never touches the container in which it is encased. Again we see how the otherwise impossible is achieved with the aid of one of nature's most useful and wonderful forces—magnetism.

Truly, a great deal of the future progress of our country depends upon magnetism and its sister force, electricity. It is well that we have learned something about them.